W0009051

CGP

KS3 Maths
Topic-based Practice Questions

It's another Quality Book from CGP

This book is packed with lots of nasty questions —
to find out what you know... and what you don't.

They're organised by topic, so you can easily test
yourself on different bits of the curriculum.

Practise getting these questions right
— you'll be doing yourself a big favour.

What CGP is all about

Our sole aim here at CGP is to produce the highest quality
books — carefully written, immaculately presented and
dangerously close to being funny.

Then we work our socks off to get them out to you
— at the cheapest possible prices.

Contents

Section One — Numbers Mostly

Multiples, Factors and Prime Factors 1
Prime Numbers 2
Special Number Sequences 3
Equivalent Fractions 4
Fractions, Decimals and Percentages 5
Rounding Off 6
Accuracy and Estimating 7
Conversion Factors 8
Metric and Imperial Units 9
Fractions 10
Percentages 12
Ratios 14
Standard Index Form Using Formulas 15
Powers (or "Indices") 16
Square Roots and Cube Roots 17
Numbers Mostly Extra Practice (1) 18
Numbers Mostly Extra Practice (2) 20

Section Two — Algebra

Turning words into Algebra 22
Basic Algebra 23
Number Patterns 27
Find the nth Term 28
Negative numbers and letters 29
Substituting Values into Formulae 30
Trial and Improvement 31
The Balance Method for Equations 32
Solving Equations 33
Rearranging Formulas 34
Density and Speed 35
x, y and z coordinates 36
Finding the Gradient of a line 37
What the Gradient means 38
Common Graphs 39
Plotting Straight Line Graphs 41
Plotting Curved Graphs 43
Interpreting Graphs 44
Factorising Quadratics 45
Simultaneous Equations 46
Inequalities 48

Graphical Inequalities 49
Algebra Extra Practice (1) 50
Algebra Extra Practice (2) 54

Section Three — Shapes

Regular Polygons 55
Symmetry 56
Shape properties 57
Areas 58
Circles 59
Perimeters and Areas 60
Volume or Capacity 61
Solids and Nets 62
Geometry 63
Circle Geometry 65
Similarity 66
Enlargement 67
Translation 68
Rotation 69
Reflection 70
Pythagoras' Theorem 71
Bearings 72
Trigonometry 73
Loci and Constructions 75
Shapes Extra Practice (1) 76
Shapes Extra Practice (2) 79

Section Four — Statistics & Probability

Probability 80
Estimating Probability 82
Combined Probability 83
Probability - Tree Diagrams 84
Graphs and Charts 85
Mean, Median, Mode and Range 87
Frequency Tables 88
Grouped Frequency Tables 89
Cumulative Frequency Tables 90
Cumulative Frequency Curves 91
Statistics & Probability Extra Practice (1) 92
Statistics & Probability Extra Practice (2) 94

Published by CGP

Contributors:

Cath Brown, Pam Chatley, Alison Chisholm, Peter Clegg, Margaret Darlington, Angela Duffy, Peter Hall, Hazel Harper, Sharon Keeley, Alan Mason, Sam Norman

With thanks to Peter Caunter and Glenn Rogers for the proofreading.
Jolly bits of clipart from CorelDRAW®

Printed by Elanders Ltd, Newcastle upon Tyne

ISBN: 978 1 84146 126 7
Groovy website: www.cgpbooks.co.uk

Based on the classic CGP style created by Richard Parsons.

Multiples, Factors and Prime Factors

1   A rectangle has an area of 24 cm².

(a) (i) Complete the table below by entering all the possible whole-number values for the length and the width of the rectangle.

Length	Width	Area
....	....	24 cm²
....	....	24 cm²
....	....	24 cm²
....	....	24 cm²

(ii) Write down all the factors of 24.

....

(b) Write down all the factors of 36.

....

2   The lowest common multiple (LCM) of 6 and 8 is 24, as it is the first number that occurs in both the 6 and 8 times tables.
Find the lowest common multiple of:

(a) 6 and 9 ....

(b) 8 and 12 ....

3 Factor trees allow you to find the prime factors of a number.

(a) Complete the factor tree.

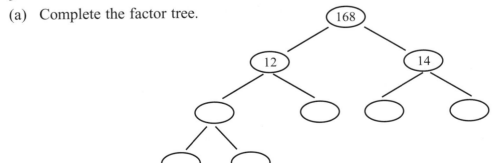

(b) Express 168 as a product of prime factors. ....

Prime Numbers

1 The factors of a number are all the numbers that divide into it.

   (a) Find all the factors of the following numbers.

   22 ....

   41 ....

   33 ....

   62 ....

   (b) Which of the four numbers above is prime?

   ....

   (c) Explain how you know it is a prime number.

   ....

2 Which is the only even prime number?

   ....

3 In the following number grid, put a cross through all the prime numbers.
   The first four have been done for you.

1	✕	✕	4	✕	6	✕	8	9	10
11	12	13	14	15	16	17	18	19	20
21	22	23	24	25	26	27	28	29	30
31	32	33	34	35	36	37	38	39	40

4 A and B are prime numbers.
   Write "T" or "F" next to the following statements to show whether they are True or False.

   (a) $A + B$ could be prime. ....   (b) $\frac{A}{B}$ is always an integer. ....

   (c) AB is never prime. ....   (d) $A - B$ is always prime. ....

Special Number Sequences

1 In the number grid opposite:

(a) Put a cross over all the square numbers.

(b) Circle all the triangular numbers.

1	2	3	4	5	6	7	8	9	10
11	12	13	14	15	16	17	18	19	20
21	22	23	24	25	26	27	28	29	30
31	32	33	34	35	36	37	38	39	40

(c) Write down all the numbers up to 40 which are both square and triangular.

....

2 X and Y are two-digit numbers. X is even and Y is odd.
Write each of the following expressions into the correct box below.
The first two have been done for you.

$X + Y$ $\qquad$ $X + 2$ $\qquad$ $Y - 1$ $\qquad$ $6Y$ $\qquad$ XY $\qquad$ $3Y$ $\qquad$ X^2 $\qquad$ $X - 7$ $\qquad$ $\dfrac{X}{X}$

ODD	EVEN
$X + Y$	$X + 2$

3 Draw lines to link the correct number with the correct description.

An odd number greater than 100 $\qquad$ 27

An even square number $\qquad$ 28

A triangular number $\qquad$ 144

An odd cube number $\qquad$ 121

Equivalent Fractions

4

1 Find the next 3 terms in these sequences.
Then state the fractions in their simplest forms.

(a) $\dfrac{2}{6} = \dfrac{3}{9} = \dfrac{4}{12} =$ .... $=$ .... $=$ ....　　Fraction in its simplest form: ....

(b) $\dfrac{6}{10} = \dfrac{9}{15} = \dfrac{12}{20} =$ .... $=$ .... $=$ ....　　Fraction in its simplest form: ....

2 Find the missing numbers below:

(a) $\dfrac{2}{9} = \dfrac{10}{a}$　　...

(b) $\dfrac{b}{7} = \dfrac{24}{56}$　　...

(c) $\dfrac{8}{9} = \dfrac{c}{72}$　　...

3 Complete the following table.

Simplified Fraction	Fraction out of one hundred	Percentage
....	$\dfrac{50}{100}$	....
....	....	70
$\dfrac{19}{20}$	....	....
....	$\dfrac{32}{100}$	....
....	....	6

4 Find the missing expressions in these algebraic fractions.

(a) $\dfrac{2a}{?} = \dfrac{8ab}{20b}$　　...

(b) $\dfrac{3x}{5x^2} = \dfrac{6xy}{?}$　　...

Fractions, Decimals and Percentages

1 Place the following numbers in order, beginning with the smallest.

$$0.12 \qquad 17\% \qquad \frac{1}{20} \qquad \frac{13}{100} \qquad 9\% \qquad \frac{9}{50}$$

....

2 Convert the following fractions into percentages.

(a) $\frac{2}{5}$ ....

(b) $\frac{17}{20}$ ....

(c) $\frac{x}{100}$ ....

3 Lydia says that if $\frac{1}{10}$ is 0.10 then $\frac{1}{8}$ is 0.8.

(a) Is she right? ....

(b) Give a reason for your answer.

....

4 Complete the following table.

Fraction	Decimal	Percentage
$\frac{19}{100}$	....	....
....	0.375	....
....	....	4
....	0.82	....
$\frac{11}{16}$	....	....

6

Rounding Off

1. The thickness of a butterfly wing is 0.0765 mm.
    Round 0.0765:

    (a) to 2 significant figures. ....

    (b) to 2 decimal places. ....

2. A newspaper reports that the attendance at a top Premiership football match was 52 000 people. If this figure is correct to 2 significant figures, circle the numbers below which could possibly have been the exact attendance.

    52 200   52 502   51 499   51 520   50 478

3. Complete the following table by rounding each number to 1, 2 and 3 significant figures.

	1 sig. fig.	2 sig. figs	3 sig. figs
5653	....	....	....
42.56	....	....	....
0.3592	....	....	....
9.995	....	....	....
0.001596	....	....	....

4. Mr Brown has bought a rectangular field for his horses.
    The field is 20 m long and 16 m wide.
    These measurements are to the nearest metre.

    (a) What is the smallest possible area of the field?

    ....

    (b) Mr Brown intends to build a fence around the outside of the field.

    What is the maximum length of fencing he will require?

    ....

SECTION ONE — NUMBERS MOSTLY

Accuracy and Estimating

1   Mrs Williams wants to buy a new carpet for her rectangular lounge.
She measures the length and the width and finds them to be 5.863 m and 3.67 m respectively.

Calculate the area of the lounge floor, giving your answer to a suitable degree of accuracy.

....

....

2   Suggest an appropriate degree of accuracy for each of the numbers in brackets.

(a) Mr Lang is (1.6298 m) tall.   .... m

(b) A car petrol tank holds (52.739 litres).   .... litres

(c) The distance between two planets is (49 657 833.87 miles).   .... miles

3   Harry is organising a school trip for 154 pupils. The cost of the transport is £614.
Harry decides that to cover the cost he must charge pupils £40 each.

(a) Use estimation to check Harry's calculation. Show all your working.

....

(b) Is Harry right?

....

4   Estimate the value of the following calculation. Show all your working.

$$\frac{5.2 \times 43}{306.9 + 99.6}$$

....

....

8

Conversion Factors

1. Two race officials are using different makes of stopwatch to time a race.
   The first official records the winning time as 3 minutes 52 seconds.
   The second official records it as 3.83 minutes.

   (a) Which is the faster time?

   ....

   (b) What is the difference between the two times in seconds?

   ....

2. Bill and Ted work for a company called "Walk On".
   They are planning a new hike for walkers on Kneesurtmoor.
   The scale of the map they are using is 1 : 50 000.

   (a) The distance between Up Hill and The Puff Inn is 6 km.
   What is the distance on the map?

   ....

   (b) The distance between the start and finish of the hike on the map is 32 cm.
   How long is the hike? Give your answer in kilometres.

   ....

3. The Tanning family are travelling to Italy for their summer holiday.
   The exchange rate when they leave is €1.63 = £1

   (a) Mr Tanning exchanges £500 without having to pay a commission fee.
   How many euros did he get in exchange?

   ....

   (b) While on holiday Mrs Tanning spends €142 on presents to take home.
   How many pounds did she spend? Give your answer to the nearest penny.

   ....

   (c) On arriving home Mr Tanning has €73 left. The exchange rate now is €1.49 = £1.
   To the nearest pound how much money does he have left?

   ....

SECTION ONE — NUMBERS MOSTLY

Metric and Imperial Units

1   Complete the following table to give the same distances on the right as on the left.

42 mm	.... cm
2450 m	.... km
392 cm	.... m
2.93 km	.... m
0.08 cm	.... mm

2   What metric and imperial units would be most appropriate for measuring the following?

	Metric Unit	Imperial Unit
Amount of water in a bath	....	....
Height of a doorway	....	....
One bag of sugar	....	....
Length of a pencil	....	....
Distance from London to Glasgow	....	....

3   Mr Evy attends his local slimming club. Since starting he has lost a total of 27 lb.

(a) How many kilograms is this?

....

(b) He needs to lose another 2 stone 3 lb to achieve his target weight.
What will his total weight loss in kilograms be?

....

....

Fractions

1 In the following table, convert the decimals to fractions.

Decimal	Fraction
0.7	....
0.23	....
0.096	....
0.08	....
1.925	....

2 Express the following fractions in their lowest terms.

(a) $\dfrac{16}{20}$ ....

(b) $\dfrac{24}{56}$ ....

3 Calculate the following:

(a) $\dfrac{2}{3} \times \dfrac{4}{11}$ ....

(b) $\dfrac{5}{8} \div \dfrac{2}{3}$ ....

4 George receives £5.00 pocket money every week. He usually spends $\frac{3}{10}$ of his money on sweets, $\frac{1}{4}$ on magazines, and $\frac{2}{5}$ on toys. He saves the rest.

(a) How much does George spend on sweets each week?

....

(b) How much money does he save each week?

....

....

Fractions

1   Cancel the following fractions to their lowest terms and then convert
each of them into decimals, with a maximum of 4 decimal places.

(a) $\dfrac{9}{24}$ ....

(b) $\dfrac{42}{45}$ ....

(c) $\dfrac{84}{18}$ ....

2   James says that $^{23}\!/_7$ is the same as $2\,^3\!/_7$.
Using your calculator, show that he is wrong.

....

3   Simplify the following expressions. Your answers should be integers or mixed numbers.

(a) $3\frac{5}{8}+1\frac{7}{16}$ ....

....

(b) $\frac{9}{10}\times1\frac{11}{12}$ ....

....

(c) $2\frac{5}{12}\div\frac{29}{24}$ ....

....

4   Find the value of x in the following equations.

(a) $\dfrac{x}{25}=\dfrac{14}{5}$ ....

(b) $4\frac{1}{2}=\dfrac{9}{x}$ ....

(c) $\dfrac{3x}{8}=\dfrac{3}{4}$ ....

Percentages

1   Find:

(a) 39% of £300   ....

(b) 20% of £14.20   ....

(c) 84% of £2.50   ....

2   The following table gives details of Liane's test results in Maths, English and Science.

Subject	Score	Possible Total	Percentage Score
Maths	46	60	....
English	75	95	....
Science	27	35	....

Complete the table by converting the scores into percentages, to 1 decimal place.

3   Mr Barker is deciding whether to retire at 55 instead of 60. His pension company says that if he retires at 55 he will only receive 82.5% of the pension he would have received at 60.
If the pension at 60 was due to be £9450 per year, how much will he receive per year if he chooses to retire at 55?

....

4   At Patterson's Plc, the directors have given all employees the choice between an extra £10 or an extra 10% per week in their wages.

Which of the following employees would be better off choosing 10%?

Mr Patel who earns £102 per week.

Miss Dalton who earns £98.50 per week.

Mrs Ferrar who earns £120 per week.

....

....

....

Percentages

1 An antique painting originally bought for £4000 is being put up for auction.

(a) The painting sells for £4400.

(i) What profit has been made?

....

(ii) What is the percentage profit?

....

(b) If the painting had sold for £3500, what would the percentage loss have been?

....

2 A car is sold with a percentage loss of 15% at a price of £1700.
What was the original price of the car?

....

....

3 The following table shows the sale price for a number of items from the Sleepeezy bedroom showrooms and also the discount applied to each item. Find the original prices to the nearest penny.

ITEM	SALE PRICE	DISCOUNT	ORIGINAL PRICE
Single Bed	£65	15%	....
Double Bed	£240	35%	....
Bunk Beds	£190	40%	....

4 At the beginning of Year 7, Lofty was 1.28 m tall. At the end of Year 9 he was 1.67 m tall.

(a) Calculate his percentage increase in height.

....

His percentage increase in height from the end of Year 9 to the
end of Year 11 is only half what it was from Year 7 to Year 9.

(b) Calculate Lofty's height at the end of Year 11.

....

Ratios

1   Simplify fully the following ratios.

   (a) 21 : 56 ....

   (b) 4.5 : 13.5 ....

   (c) £3.60 : £4.20 ....

   (d) 7 cm : 49 mm ....

2   Mrs Cooke has a secret cake recipe which contains two ingredients, X and Y.
   To make the perfect cake, the ratio of X to Y must be 5 : 13.

   (a) How many times more of Y must there be than X?

   ....

   The combined ingredients must weigh a total of 144 g.

   (b) What weight must there be of ingredient Y?

   ....

   ....

   (c) For every gram of ingredient Y, what weight of ingredient X will be needed?

   ....

3   The famous boy band, Eastalive, has three singers.
   When they perform live, the microphones A, B and C must be
   balanced in the ratio $x : 2x : x + 3$ to create their unique sound.
   The total power output for the three singers is to be 42 watts.

   (a) Calculate the power connected to microphone A.

   ....

   ....

   (b) How many times more power is connected to microphone C than to microphone A?

   ....

Standard Index Form

1   Express the following numbers in standard form.

(a) 98 450   ....

(b) 8.3   ....

(c) 0.0064   ....

(d) 0.97   ....

2   The following table shows information about the area and population of four countries.

COUNTRY	POPULATION	AREA (km²)
Canada	3.1×10^7	1.0×10^7
France	6.0×10^7	5.5×10^5
India	1.0×10^9	3.3×10^6
United Kingdom	6.0×10^7	2.4×10^5

(a) Write down the country with the largest population.   ....

(b) Write down the country with the smallest area.   ....

(c) How many more people per km² are there in India than in the United Kingdom?

    ....

    ....

3      $\dfrac{1}{2000} = 0.0005$

(a) Write 0.0005 in standard form.   ....

(b) Write $\dfrac{1}{20\ 000}$ in standard form.   ....

(c) Work out $\dfrac{1}{2000} + \dfrac{1}{20\ 000}$ in standard form.   ....

    ....

Powers (or "Indices")

1 Simplify the following. Leave your answers in index form.

(a) $3^4 \times 3^2$ ....

(b) $\dfrac{5^8}{5^5}$ ....

(c) $(2^6)^3$ ....

(d) $27^{\frac{1}{3}}$ ....

2 Evaluate the following expressions:

(a) $\dfrac{(m^2)^4 \times m^3 \times 1^{65}}{m^0 \times (m^3)^3}$ when $m = 2$. ....

....

(b) $\dfrac{\left(\dfrac{y^{10}}{y^8}\right) \times (y^2)^5}{(y^2)^2 \times y^4}$ when $y = 3$. ....

....

3 Look at this table:

9^1	9
9^2	81
9^3	729
9^4	6561
9^5	59 049
9^6	531 441
9^7	4 782 969
9^8	43 046 721

(a) Explain how the table shows that $729 \times 6561 = 4\ 782\ 969$.

....

(b) Use the table to help you work out the value of:

(i) $\dfrac{43\ 046\ 721}{531\ 441}$ ....

(ii) 729×81 ....

Square Roots and Cube Roots

1 Evaluate the following to two decimal places.

(a) $142^{\frac{1}{3}}$ ....

(b) $142^{\frac{1}{2}}$ ....

(c) $\sqrt{82}$ ....

(d) $\sqrt[3]{1986}$ ....

2 The volume of a cube is given by the following formula:

$$V = S^3 \qquad \text{(where } V = \text{volume and } S = \text{side length)}$$

From the given volumes, calculate the side lengths of the following cubes.
Give your answers to 3 significant figures.

(a) 400 cm³ ....

(b) 12 680 m³ ....

(c) 12 mm³ ....

3 $(y^2)^3 = y^{(2 \times 3)}$ and $m^{\frac{1}{3}} = \sqrt[3]{m}$

(a) Use this information to explain in words the meaning of the following expression:

$G^{\frac{2}{3}}$ ....

(b) Evaluate:

(i) $8^{\frac{2}{3}}$ ....

(ii) $27^{\frac{2}{3}}$ ....

(iii) $125^{\frac{2}{3}}$ ....

Numbers Mostly Extra Practice (1)

1 In each of the following, fill in the missing number.

(a) $\frac{1}{2}$ of 30 = $\frac{1}{4}$ of ....

(b) $\frac{3}{5}$ of 100 = $\frac{1}{2}$ of ....

(c) $\frac{1}{3}$ of 90 = $\frac{2}{3}$ of ....

2 On a farm 60 sheep gave birth. 35% of the sheep gave birth to two lambs.
The rest of the sheep gave birth to just one lamb.
In total how many lambs were born?

....

....

3 Look at the following numbers.

$$1^6 \quad 2^5 \quad 3^4 \quad 4^3 \quad 5^3 \quad 6^1$$

(a) (i) Which is the largest? ....

(ii) Which is equal to 9^2? ....

(b) Which two of the numbers below are not square numbers?

$$2^4 \quad 2^5 \quad 2^6 \quad 2^7 \quad 2^8$$

....

4 The table shows some percentages of amounts of money.

	£10	£30	£45
5%	50p	£1.50	£2.25
10%	£1	£3	£4.50

Use the table to help fill in the missing numbers.

(a) 15% of £30 = ...   (b) £6.75 = 15% of ....

(c) £10.50 = ... % of £30   (d) 25p = 5% of ....

Numbers Mostly Extra Practice (1)

5 This question is about estimation.

(a) Look at the following numbers:

6   7   8   9   10   11

Circle the best estimate of the answer to: $\dfrac{72.34}{8.91}$

....

(b) Look at the following numbers:

1.2   1.6   12   16   120   160

Circle the best estimate of the answer to 32.7×0.48.

....

Giving your answer to 1 significant figure:

(c) Estimate the answer to: $\dfrac{8.62 + 22.1}{5.23}$ ....

(d) Estimate the answer to: $\dfrac{28.6 \times 24.4}{5.67 \times 4.02}$ ....

6 Find the value of g in the following equations:

(a) $\dfrac{2}{16} = \dfrac{g}{8}$ ....

(b) $\dfrac{1}{2} = \dfrac{12}{g}$ ....

7 Consider all the whole numbers between 40 and 50 inclusive.

(a) Write down a multiple of 5 within this range which is also a triangular number.

....

(b) Write down all the prime numbers between 40 and 50.

....

Numbers Mostly Extra Practice (2)

1 The table below shows the average weekly earnings for men and women in 1950 and 1995.

	1950	**1995**
MEN	£12.56	£430.50
WOMEN	£5.93	£316.75

(a) For 1950, calculate the average weekly earnings for women as a percentage of the average weekly earnings for men. Give your answer to 1 decimal place.

....

(b) For 1995, show that the average weekly earnings for women were a greater proportion of the average weekly earnings for men than they were in 1950.

....

2 The masses of four planets are given below:

Earth 5.99×10^{24} kg
Jupiter 1.25×10^{27} kg
Saturn 5.69×10^{26} kg
Venus 4.87×10^{24} kg

(a) Which of these planets has a mass which is approximately 95 times that of the Earth?

....

(b) The radius of the Earth is approximately 6.4×10^6 m.

The volume of a sphere is given by $V = \dfrac{4}{3} \times 3.142 \times (\text{radius})^3$.

Calculate the volume of the Earth.
Give your answer in standard form correct to 3 significant figures.

....

....

3 A shop had a sale. All prices were reduced by 15%. A pair of shoes cost £38.25 in the sale. What price were the shoes before the sale?

....

Numbers Mostly Extra Practice (2)

4   Mr and Mrs Gitawhey are travelling to America for their summer holiday.
     At the time of leaving the exchange rate is £1 = $1.62.
     They change £1800 into dollars without having to pay a commission fee.

(a) How many dollars will they have?

     ....

     When they return home they have $126 remaining. The exchange rate now is £1 = $1.78.

(b) If the financial brokers charge a 10% handling fee, how many pounds do they return home with?

     ....

     ....

5   In the triangle below, the length of the longest side *x* is found using the following formula:

$$x = \sqrt{y^2 + z^2}$$

     If *y* = 4.3 km and *z* = 9.63 km, how long is side *x*?

     ....

6   For this question, use the following conversions:
             36 inches = 0.9 metres
             1 kilogram = 2.2 pounds
             1 gallon = 4.5 litres

(a) Mr Roe is struggling with the metric system. He knows his car will hold 12 gallons of petrol.

     How many litres is this? ....

(b) In a recent medical he weighed 192 lb.

     What was his weight in kilograms? ....

(c) The doctor also measured his height and found it to be 1.83 m.

     Calculate this height in feet and inches to the nearest inch.

     ....

SECTION TWO — ALGEBRA

Turning Words into Algebra

1. Diahann asks Tommy how old he is. He replies, "If you treble my age, then subtract 17, the answer is 28."

   (a) Let T be Tommy's age. Write an equation for T.

   ....

   Diahann works out how old Tommy is. Tommy then asks her how old she is.
   She says, "If you take double your age away from 46, you get my age."

   (b) Let D be Diahann's age. Write an equation relating D and T.

   ....

2. My monthly telephone bill is made up of two charges:

   > Line rental of £10 per month.
   > Call charges of 6p per call.

   Last month, my bill came to £16.48. How many calls did I make?

   ....

   ....

3. Palvi, Laura and Sarah all have Saturday jobs as waitresses. They all get paid £x per hour.
   Last Saturday, they all worked for 5 hours. Palvi got £4.50 in tips, Laura got £5.20 and
   Sarah got £2.30. At the end of the day, they put all the money they had earned together,
   and shared it out between them. Each girl ended up with £24.

   (a) How much money did the three girls get in total?

   ....

   (b) Use the information to write an equation for x.

   ....

   (c) Solve your equation to find the value of x.

   ....

   ....

Basic Algebra

1   Simplify the following.

(a) $4x - 2y + 3x + y =$ ....

(b) $2x^2 - 2x + 6x - 5 - x^3 + 4x^2 =$ ....

(c) $2ab - a + b + 2a - 6ab + 2b + b^2 =$ ....

2   Multiply out these brackets.

(a) $2(5x - 1) =$ ....

(b) $6x(4x - 3y) =$ ....

(c) $-8a(2a - b) =$ ....

(d) $-3w(2x + 5y) =$ ....

(e) $xy(6x - y) =$ ....

3   The lawn in John's garden is rectangular, and has sides of length $3x$ and $x + 4$.

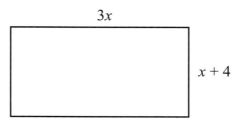

(a) Write a formula for the perimeter P of the lawn. Simplify your answer.

....

(b) Write a formula for the area A of the lawn. Expand and simplify your answer.

....

Basic Algebra

1   Expand these brackets.

    (a) $(x + 3)(x + 6) =$ ....

    (b) $(x + 4)(x + 9) =$ ....

    (c) $(x + 4)(x - 3) =$ ....

    (d) $(x - 3)(x + 3) =$ ....

    (e) $(x - 5)(x - 2) =$ ....

2   Expand these brackets.

    (a) $(2x + 1)(x + 2) =$ ....

    (b) $(3x + 2)(2x + 5) =$ ....

    (c) $(2x - 3)(x + 4) =$ ....

    (d) $(4x - 5)(x - 1) =$ ....

    (e) $(2x + 1)(2x - 1) =$ ....

3   David has been having some problems with his homework.
       Explain what he has got wrong, and then do the question correctly.

    (a) $(3x - 1)(x + 1) = 3x^2 - x + 3x + 1 = 3x^2 + 2x + 1$

      ....

      ....

    (b) $(5x + 3)(3x + 2) = 8x^2 + 7x + 6x + 5 = 8x^2 + 13x + 5$

      ....

      ....

Basic Algebra

1   Expand the following brackets and simplify your answers as much as possible.

(a) $(x + 2)(x + 3) =$ ....

(b) $(2x - 1)(x - 6) =$ ....

(c) $(a + 2b)(2a - b) =$ ....

(d) $(x - 2)(2x^2 + 1) =$ ....

(e) $(13x - 4)(17x + 9) =$ ....

2   Expand and simplify.

(a) $(x + 2)^2 =$ ....

....

(b) $(2a - b)^2 =$ ....

....

(c) $(25x - 6)^2 =$ ....

....

3   Jan thinks of a number. She doubles it, then adds 3. Then she squares the result.
She tells the answer to Sadiq.

(a) Let x stand for the number Jan thinks of. Write down a formula for the answer she tells Sadiq.

....

(b) Expand and simplify your answer from (a).

....

....

Basic Algebra

1   Factorise the following.

    (a) $2x^2 - 4x =$ ....

    (b) $3xy^2 - 5x^2y =$ ....

    (c) $8ab - 2b^2 + 10bc =$ ....

    (d) $4x - 8y =$ ....

2   The rectangle below has an area of $6xy - 10y$.

> Area $= 6xy - 10y$

    (a) Factorise $6xy - 10y$.

    ....

    (b) If one side of the rectangle has length y, write down the length of the other side.

    ....

3   Kulvinder thinks of a number, x.
He squares the number, then adds four times the number he first thought of.
He tells the answer to Rosalita.

    (a) Write down a formula for the number Kulvinder tells Rosalita.

    ....

    (b) Factorise your formula.

    ....

Number Patterns

1 Find the next two terms in each of the following sequences.

(a) 5, 8, 11, 14, 17, ... , ...

(b) 100, 90, 82, 76, 72, ... , ...

(c) 100, 10, 1, 0.1, 0.01, ... , ...

2 The diagram shows some patterns of black and grey squares.
The fourth pattern has been left blank.

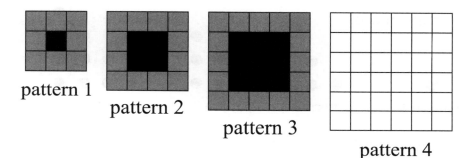

pattern 1   pattern 2   pattern 3   pattern 4

(a) Draw the fourth pattern on the blank grid.

(b) Write down the numbers of black squares and grey squares in the fifth pattern.

Black squares ....

Grey squares ....

3 Find the next two terms in each of the following sequences.

(a) 106, 107, 213, 320, 533, 853, ... , ...

(b) 5, 15, 35, 75, 155, 315, ... , ...

(c) 1.8, 1.77, 1.74, 1.71, 1.68, ... , ...

Finding the nth Term

1 Find the nth term of the following sequences.

(a) 2, 4, 6, 8, ….

....

(b) 1, 3, 5, 7, ….

....

(c) 12, 10, 8, 6, ….

....

2 Look at these patterns of dots.

pattern 1   pattern 2   pattern 3   pattern 4

Find a formula for the number of dots in the nth pattern.

....

....

3 Write down the nth terms for these sequences.

(a) 1, 4, 9, 16, ….

....

(b) 3, 5, 7, 9, ….

....

(c) 1×3, 4×5, 9×7, 16×9, ….

(Use your answers to (a) and (b) to work out the nth term of this sequence.)

....

Negative Numbers and Letters

1   Work out each of the following.

   (a) $-5 \times -2 =$ ....

   (b) $-5 + -7 - 6 =$ ....

   (c) $10 - -4 + 5 =$ ....

   (d) $-12 \div 3 =$ ....

   (e) $-4 \times -100 \div -25 =$ ....

2   Simplify the following.

   (a) $-2x - 3x + 4x - 10x =$ ....

   (b) $(4x - -5x) \div (-2 - 1) =$ ....

   (c) $8y \div -4 + -8x \div 2 =$ ....

3   If $x = -4$ and $y = 3$, work out the values of the following expressions.

   (a) $x^2 y$

   ....

   (b) $(xy)^2$

   ....

   (c) $x^2 - y^2$

   ....

   (d) $y^3 + x^3 - 2xy$

   ....

Substituting Values into Formulas

1   This formula relates distance travelled, d, starting speed, s, acceleration, a, and time taken, t:

$$d = st + \frac{1}{2}at^2$$

Find the distance travelled if the starting speed was 2 m/s, the acceleration was 0.5 m/s² and the time taken was 10 s.

....

....

2   The formula for the time (in minutes) required to cook a turkey that weighs W kilograms is:

$$T = \frac{75W + 990}{11}$$

(a) Find the time required to cook a 4 kg turkey to the nearest minute.

....

....

(b) The formula for converting weight in pounds (P) into weight in kilograms (W) is:

$$W = \frac{5P}{11}$$

How long, to the nearest minute, will a 16.5 pound turkey take to cook?

....

....

....

3   Here is a formula connecting H, A, B and C.

$$H = AC^2 + 2B - \frac{2B + C}{3A}$$

Find H when $A = 2$, $B = 10\frac{1}{2}$ and $C = -3$.

....

....

Trial and Improvement

1 The equation $x^3 - 5x^2 + 3 = 0$ has a solution between 0 and 1.
Find the solution to 1 decimal place. You may find the table below helpful.

x	x^3	$5x^2$	$x^3 - 5x^2$	$x^3 - 5x^2 + 3$	
0	0	0	0	3	Too big
1	1	5	−4	−1	Too small

2 The diagram below shows a box. The lengths of its sides, in cm, are y, $y + 1$ and $4y - 2$.

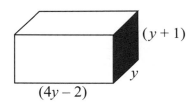

The volume of the box is 28 120 cm³. y is an integer. Find the value of y.

The Balance Method for Equations

1 Write down step-by-step solutions to the following equations.
   You must show **all** your working.

(a) $2x + 8 = 4 - 6x$

   ....

   ....

(b) $6(x - 1) = 42$

   ....

   ....

(c) $4 - 10x = 9$

   ....

   ....

(d) $\dfrac{6}{2x - 1} = 2$

   ....

   ....

   ....

(e) $4 - \dfrac{12}{5x - 1} = 6$

   ....

   ....

   ....

Solving Equations

1   Solve the following equations.

(a) $4(x-2) - 2(3-2x) = 5x + 1$

....

....

....

(b) $\dfrac{6}{2x-1} = \dfrac{8}{3x-2}$

....

....

....

(c) $\sqrt{1-2x} = 3$

....

....

2   I am thinking of a number. I square my number, then add 7, then take the square root of this number. The answer I get is one more than my original number.

(a)   Using x to stand for my original number, write this as an equation.

....

(b)   Solve the equation to find the number I was thinking of.

....

....

....

Rearranging Formulas

1 The formula $V = \frac{1}{3}\pi r^2 h$ is used to calculate the volume of a cone.

   (a) Rearrange the formula to make h the subject.

....

....

   (b) Rearrange the formula to make r the subject.

....

....

2 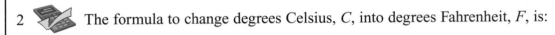 The formula to change degrees Celsius, C, into degrees Fahrenheit, F, is:

$$\boxed{F = 1.8C + 32}$$

   (a) Rearrange the formula to make C the subject.

....

   (b) Change 80 degrees Fahrenheit into degrees Celsius.

....

....

3 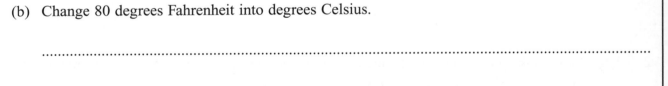 The formula $d = st + \frac{1}{2}at^2$ is used to calculate the distance travelled by an object.

   Make a the subject of the formula.

....

....

Density and Speed

1 Calculate the density of these materials:

(a) A mass of 300 kg of gold alloy with a volume of 0.02 m³.

....

(b) A mass of 1800 kg of aluminium with a volume of 0.6 m³.

....

2 Find the distance travelled in each of the following cases.

(a) A bus going at a speed of 70 km/h for 4 hours.

....

(b) A man cycling at 15 km/h for 3½ hours.

....

(c) A boat travelling at a speed of 160 mph for 15 minutes.

....

3 The density of oil in a tank is 800 kg/m³. The mass of the oil is 20 tonnes.
Calculate the volume of oil in the tank (1 tonne = 1000 kg).

....

....

4 At 4 pm Claire set off in her car on a journey of 180 miles to the airport.
She arrived there at 7 pm. Calculate her average speed in miles per hour.

....

....

X, Y and Z Coordinates

1 The points A, B and C are three of the vertices of a parallelogram ABCD.

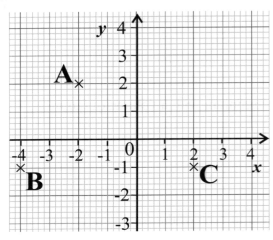

(a) Write down the coordinates of A, B and C.

A = ...   B = ...   C = ...

(b) Write down the coordinates of the fourth vertex, D, of the parallelogram. ....

(c) What is the area of the parallelogram ABCD?

....

2 The cuboid in the diagram is of length 4 units, width 3 units and height 2 units.

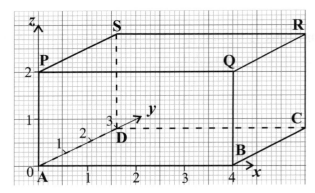

(a) Write down the coordinates of the points B, R, S and P.

B = ...   R = ...   S = ...   P = ...

(b) Write down the coordinates of the mid-points of AB, CD and SR.

AB = ...   CD = ...   SR = ...

Finding the Gradient of a Line

1 Use the grid on the right to answer the question below.

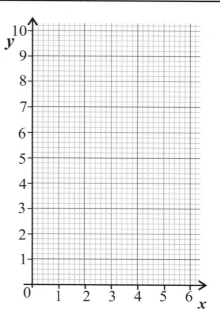

(a) Plot the points A(1, 2), B(5, 3), C(0, 10) and D(5, 7).

(b) Find the gradient of the line joining these points:

　(i)　A and B. ....

　(ii)　C and D. ....

2 Add points B and Q to the grid below so that:

(a) The line AB has a gradient of 2.

(b) The line PQ has a gradient of –3.

3 Find the value of *a* if the line joining the points (4, 2*a*) and (10, 4*a*) has a gradient of 2.

....

....

What the Gradient Means

1 This graph can be used to convert pounds into US dollars ($).
Use the graph to answer the following questions.

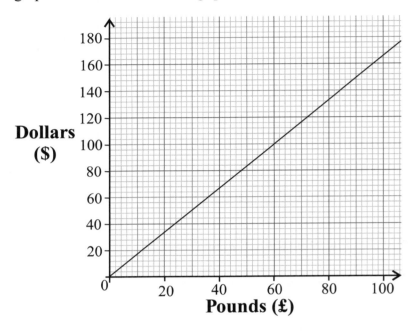

(a) Convert £50 to dollars. ....

(b) What is the gradient of the graph? ....

(c) What is the exchange rate in dollars per pound? ....

2 Paul travels to his friend's house. He cycles the first part of the journey,
then he travels by train and he does the last part of the journey on foot.

Which of the graphs above is most likely to represent his journey? ....

Common Graphs

1 The diagram below shows a square with vertices A, B, C and D.

Match each line with the correct equation.

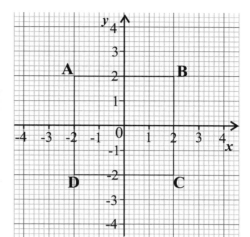

$y = 2$ line DB

$x = -2$ line DC

$y = x$ line AB

$y = -2$ line AD

$y = -x$ line AC

2 Choose the correct line (P, Q, R, S or T) for each of the following equations.

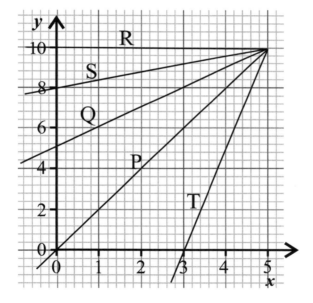

(a) $y = x + 5$ ....

(b) $5y = 2x + 40$ ....

(c) $y = 10$ ....

(d) $y = 2x$ ....

(e) $y = 5x - 15$ ....

Common Graphs

1 Here are five equations.

$$y = x - 3 \qquad y = x^2 + 5 \qquad y = \frac{2}{x} \qquad y = x^3 \qquad y = 5 - 2x$$

(a) Label each graph with the correct equation from above.

   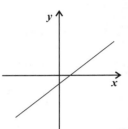

A = ...   B = ...   C = ...   D = ...

(b) On the axes below, sketch the graph of the equation that is **not** drawn above.

2 Below are four equations and their graphs.

$$y = x^3 - 1 \qquad x + y = 10 \qquad y = x^2 + 4 \qquad y = 2x + 6$$

   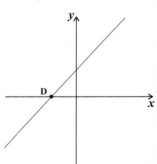

Write down the coordinates of the points A, B, C and D.

A = ...   B = ...   C = ...   D = ...

Plotting Straight Line Graphs

1   The graph of $y = 3x - 2$ is a straight line.

(a) Complete this table of values for the equation $y = 3x - 2$.

x	0	3	5
y			

(b) Plot the graph $y = 3x - 2$ on the axes below.

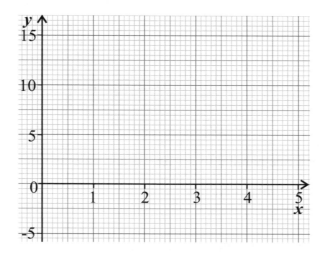

(c) Write down the point of intersection of the graph with the x-axis. ....

2   The graph of $x + y = 4$ is also a straight line.

(a) The equation $x + y = 4$ can be written in a different way.
Tick the correct way below.

☐ $x = y + 4$ ☐ $y = x + 4$ ☐ $x = y - 4$ ☐ $y = 4 - x$

(b) Complete the table of values for the equation $x + y = 4$

x	0	2	4
y			

(c) Plot the graph $x + y = 4$ on the axes below.

Plotting Straight Line Graphs

1 $y = mx + c$ is the general equation for a straight line graph.

   (a) On these axes, draw and label
the graph of $y = 3x + 1$.

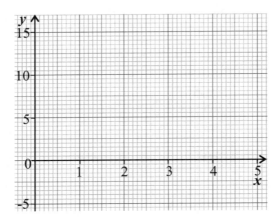

   (b) On the same axes draw a line parallel to $y = 3x + 1$ and passing through the point $(0, -3)$.

   (c) Write down the equation of this line. ....

2 Here is the table of values for the graph $y = ax + b$.

x	0	2	4
y	3	11	19

   (a) Plot these points on the axes on the right
and join them with a straight line.

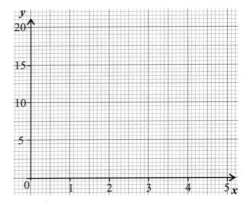

   (b) Find the values of a and b. $a =$ .... $b =$ ....

3 ABC is an isosceles triangle of perpendicular height 2 units.

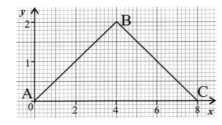

   (a) Find the equation of the line AB. ....

   (b) Find the equation of the line BC. ....

Plotting Curved Graphs

1   The graph of the equation $y = x^2 + 3x - 9$ is a curve.

(a) Complete the table of values for the equation $y = x^2 + 3x - 9$.

x	-3	-2	-1	0	1	2	3
y							

(b) On the axes, plot the points shown in the table and join them up to form a smooth curve.

(c) What is the minimum value of y?

....

(d) What is the value of y when $x = 1.5$?

....

2   The graph of the equation $y = 2x^2 - 6x + 5$ is also a curve.

(a) Complete the table of values for the equation $y = 2x^2 - 6x + 5$.

x	-3	-2	-1	0	1	2	3
y							

(b) On the axes below, plot the points shown in the table and join them up to form a smooth curve.

(c) State the line of symmetry of the graph. ....

Interpreting Graphs

1 A garage sells petrol at £0.75 per litre.

(a) Complete the table of values for the cost of petrol.

Litres (L)	0	10	20	30	40
Cost (C)					

(b) On the axes draw a graph showing the relationship between L and C.

(c) Use your graph to answer the following questions.

    (i) What is the cost of 27 litres of petrol?

    ....

    (ii) How much petrol can I buy for £28?

    ....

2 The graph shows a journey of a van and a car starting at Town A, travelling to Town B and returning to Town A.

car ----   van ——

Use the graph to answer the following questions.

(a) For how long was the car stationary during the journey? ....

(b) At what time did the car overtake the van? ....

(c) At what speed was the car travelling between 10:00 and 10:30?

....

(d) What was the greatest speed reached by the van during the journey?

....

Factorising Quadratics

1 Factorise the following.

   (a) $x^2 + 8x + 12 =$ ....

   (b) $x^2 + 17x + 16 =$ ....

   (c) $x^2 - 4x + 4 =$ ....

   (d) $x^2 - 2x - 15 =$ ....

2 Solve the following equations.

   (a) $(x - 2)(x - 3) = 0$ ....

   (b) $(x + 1)(x - 2) = 0$ ....

   (c) $x^2 + 9x - 10 = 0$ ....

   ....

   (d) $x^2 + 13x + 42 = 0$ ....

   ....

3 Rearrange these equations so that they equal zero, then solve them.

   (a) $x^2 + 3x = 4$ ....

   ....

   (b) $x^2 - 6x = -8$ ....

   ....

   (c) $x^2 + 10 = -7x$ ....

   ....

Simultaneous Equations

1 Solve these simultaneous equations. You may wish to rearrange some of them first.

(a) $3x + y = 10$ $\qquad$ $x + y = 4$

....

....

(b) $12x - 11y = 23$ $\qquad$ $x + y = 0$

....

....

(c) $y = 3x + 1$ $\qquad$ $2x + 5y = 22$

....

....

2 Solve these problems by constructing simultaneous equations.

(a) Three cups of coffee and two cups of tea cost £2.70. One cup of coffee and one cup of tea costs £1.10. Work out the price of a single cup of tea.

....

....

....

(b) A shop sells two different coloured pens. The shopkeeper has forgotten the price of the pens. He can remember that three red pens and five blue pens costs £2.15 and two red pens and one blue pen costs 85p. Work out the cost of a single red pen.

....

....

....

Simultaneous Equations

1 The graphical method can also be used to solve simultaneous equations.

(a) Draw the graphs of $y = 3x + 1$ and $y = 7 - x$. Make your axes for x and y go from 0 to 10.

(b) Use your graphs to solve the simultaneous equations. $x = $ .... $y = $ ....

2 Look at the diagram below. Use it to solve the following simultaneous equations.

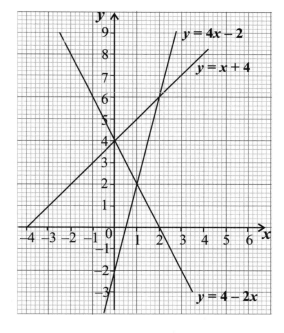

(a) $y = x + 4$ $y = 4x - 2$ $x = $ .... $y = $ ....

(b) $y = x + 4$ $y = 4 - 2x$ $x = $ .... $y = $ ....

(c) $y = 4x - 2$ $y + 2x = 4$ $x = $ .... $y = $ ....

Inequalities

1 Solve these inequalities.

(a) $3x < 12$ ....

(b) $2x + 5 < 7$ ....

(c) $7x - 4 < 24$ ....

(d) $5x - 12 \geq 18$ ....

(e) $6x + 18 \leq 48$ ....

(f) $10 - x > 4$ ....

(g) $-3x > 9$ ....

(h) $10 - 3x \geq 19$ ....

(i) $13x + 5 > 15x + 21$ ....

(j) $4x + 12 \geq 5x + 13$ ....

2 Solve these inequalities and represent the answers on a number line.

(a) $2x < 8$ ....

(b) $10 + 2x < 12$ ....

(c) $20 + 4x > 16$ ....

Graphical Inequalities

1 On the axis below, shade the region represented by $y < 3$, $y > x$ and $y < 3x - 1$.

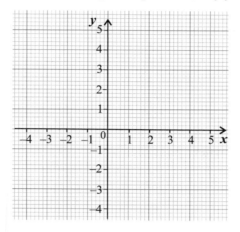

2 On the axis below, shade the region represented by $y < 5$, $y > 1$, $y > 3x - 6$ and $y > 6 - 3x$.

3 Write down the inequalities for the region shaded on the graph below.

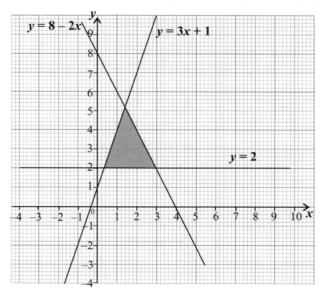

Algebra Extra Practice (1)

1 Paul is *x* years old. Write the following using algebra.

(a) Three times Paul's age. ....

(b) Paul's age six years ago. ....

2 Expand the brackets and simplify where possible.

(a) $x(2x + 2) + 4(x + 6)$ = ...

(b) $(3x - 1)(x - 7)$ = ...

(c) $(3x + 5)^2$ = ...

....

3 Look at the graph below.

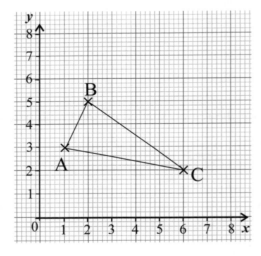

(a) Write down the coordinates of the three points on the graph.

A = ...   B = ...   C = ...

(b) Find the gradient of the line joining the following points:

(i) A to B ....

(ii) B to C ....

Algebra Extra Practice (1)

4 Factorise the following expressions.

(a) $12x + 18 = $ ....

(b) $12ab + 6b^2 = $ ....

(c) $15x^4y^3 + 5xy^2 = $ ....

5 James has invented an equation linking a, b, c and x as shown.

$$c = \frac{(x+a)^2}{b}$$

(a) If $a = 1$, $b = 2$ and $x = 3$, what does c equal?

....

(b) Find the value of b when $c = 4$, $x = 6$ and $a = 2$.

....

6 Solve the following equations.

(a) $8x + 12 = 4x + 16$

....

(b) $\dfrac{3}{2x+1} = \dfrac{1}{x-1}$

....

....

7 Rearrange these equations to make y the subject.

(a) $y^2 + 5 = x$ ....

(b) $3y + 5x + 10 = 0$ ....

Algebra Extra Practice (1)

8 Work out the next three terms in the following series.

(a) 2, 5, 10, 17, ... , ... , ...

(b) 1, 1, 2, 3, 5, ... , ... , ...

9 Write down the nth terms for the following.

(a) 6, 11, 16, 21, ...

....

(b) 2, 8, 18, 32, ...

....

10 Solve these inequalities.

(a) $12 - x \geq 20$ ....

(b) $3 + 2x < 33 + 5x$ ....

11 Draw and label these graphs on the axes below.

(a) $y = -x$ (b) $y = 3x$ (c) $y = 6$ (d) $y = 2x + 4$

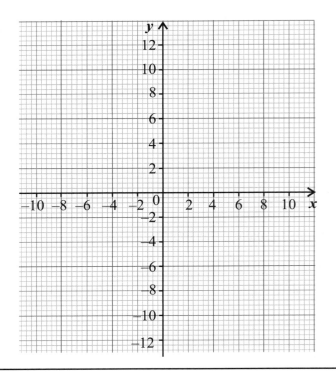

Algebra Extra Practice (1)

12 Solve these equations.

(a) $x^2 - 11x + 30 = 0$ ....

....

(b) $x^2 + 6x - 7 = 0$ ....

....

13 This question is about solving simultaneous equations.

(a) Draw the graphs of the equations $y = 3x + 1$ and $y = x + 3$.

(b) Use your graphs from part (a) to solve the simultaneous equations.

$x =$ .... $y =$ ....

(c) The two equations above can be rearranged to $y - 3x = 1$ and $y - x = 3$.
Use algebra to solve these simultaneous equations.

....

....

14 Shade the region represented by $x < 5$, $y < x$ and $y > 4 - \frac{1}{2}x$.

Algebra Extra Practice (2)

1   Solve $x^3 + x = 12$ by trial and improvement. Give your answer for x correct to 1 decimal place. Use the table below to help you.

x	x^3	$x^3 + x$	
0	0	0	Too small
3	27	30	Too big

....

2 Iron has a density of 7.9 g/cm³. Gold has a density of 19.3 g/cm³.

(a) I have a piece of metal that has a volume of 200 cm³ and a mass of 3.86 kg. Is it gold or iron?

....

(b) What is the volume of a 200 g piece of iron?

....

3 In the gym, Andy can run at 12.6 km/h.

(a) How far can Andy run in 20 minutes?

....

(b) How many minutes does it take Andy to run 8190 m?

....

....

Regular Polygons

1 Here is a regular polygon.

(a) What is the name of this shape? ....

(b) How many lines of symmetry does it have? ....

(c) What is its order of rotational symmetry? ....

2 A regular polygon has five sides. Calculate the size of one of its interior angles.

....

3 ABCDEFGH is a regular octagon. Find:

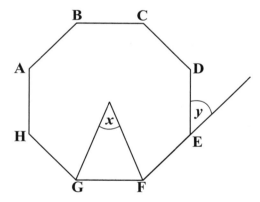

(a) x, the angle at the centre.

....

....

(b) y, the exterior angle.

....

....

4 The diagram shows part of a regular polygon.

150° (not to scale)

How many sides does it have?

....

Symmetry

1   Look at the following shapes.

    (i)   (ii)   (iii)   (iv)   (v)

   (a)   Draw all the lines of symmetry on each of the shapes.

   (b)   What is the order of rotational symmetry for each shape?

       (i) ....   (ii) ....   (iii) ....   (iv) ....   (v) ....

2   A prism has a regular hexagon as its cross-section.
How many planes of symmetry does this solid have?

....

3   The solid shown has just one plane of symmetry. Draw it on the diagram.

4   Each of these shapes should have rotational symmetry of order 4.

Draw in the necessary lines to make them correct.

Shape Properties

1   Fill in the missing numbers.

  (a)   A kite has .... pairs of adjacent sides which are equal.

      It has .... line(s) of symmetry and rotational symmetry of order ....

  (b)   An isosceles triangle has .... equal sides and .... line(s) of symmetry.

2   A right-angled triangle has one line of symmetry. What are its three angles?

    ....

3   Fill in the missing words.

  (a)   A triangle-based pyramid is called a ....

  (b)   A pyramid with a circle for a base is a ....

  (c)   A prism with a cross-section in the shape of a rectangle is a ....

4   Give the full names of the following three solids.

           (a)   (b)   (c)

  (a)   ....

  (b)   ....

  (c)   ....

5   The mathematical name for a ball is a ....

Areas

1 The diagram shows the side of a house.
The shape is a combination of an isosceles triangle and a rectangle.

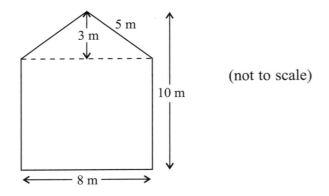

(not to scale)

Find the area of:

(a) the triangle. ....

(b) the rectangle. ....

2 This shape is made up of two identical parallelograms.

(not to scale)

Find the area of the shape.

....

....

3 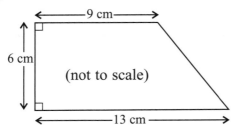 Find the area of the trapezium below.

....

....

....

Circles

1 Label the parts of the circle indicated.

2 The diameter of the Sun at its equator is 865 000 miles.
What is the circumference around its equator? Use $\pi = 3.14$.

....

....

3 A circular table top has a diameter of 80 cm.

Find the area of the table top. Use $\pi = 3.14$.

....

....

4 The Andersons want to build a circular pond in their garden. They mark out the rim of the pond
using a stake pushed into the ground and a taut piece of string with a length of 1.6 m, as shown.

What will be the circumference of their pond? Use $\pi = 3.14$.

....

....

....

....

Perimeters and Areas

1 The floor plan of the ground floor of a house is shown below. Find its perimeter.

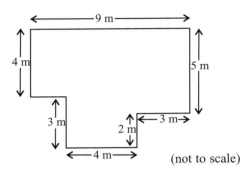

(not to scale)

....

....

....

....

2 The following shape consists of a polygon and a semicircle.

(not to scale)

Taking $\pi = 3.14$, find:

(a) the perimeter of the shape.

....

....

(b) the area of the shape.

....

....

3 The rectangular sheet of metal below has two circles cut out.

(not to scale)

R = 3.0 cm   r = 1.5 cm

Taking $\pi = 3.14$, find the area of the remaining metal.

....

....

....

Volume or Capacity

1 A triangular prism has a cross-sectional area of 18 cm² and a length of 6 cm.
   What is its volume? Include the correct units in your answer.

   ....

2 The crate below is used to transport car parts all over the world. It is cuboid-shaped.

0.5 m

0.8 m

2.4 m

   Find the volume of the crate. Include the correct units in your answer.

   ....

   ....

3 The cross-section of a tin of baked beans is a circle with a diameter of 7.4 cm.

   (a) Taking $\pi = 3.14$, find the area of the cross-section.

   ....

   (b) The tin is 11 cm high. What is its volume?

   ....

4 The first column of the table contains formulas. Some you will recognise, some you may not.
   Tick the boxes to show whether the formulas represent length, area or volume.
   D, a, l, R, r, h and w are all lengths.

FORMULA	LENGTH	AREA	VOLUME
πD			
$a^2 l$			
$2R$			
$\pi r^2 h$			
lw			

Solids and Nets

1 The diagram below shows a triangular prism. State the number of:

(a) vertices ....

(b) faces ....

(c) edges ....

2 Look at the cuboid and net below.

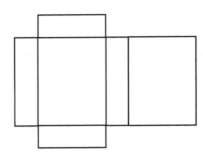

3 cm

8 cm

5 cm

Use the net to find the total surface area.

....

....

3 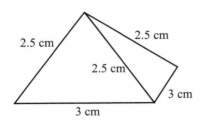 All four side faces in the square-based pyramid below are isosceles triangles.

2.5 cm

2.5 cm

2.5 cm

3 cm

3 cm

Draw a net of the solid.
Label each side with its length.

Geometry

1. Find angles *a* and *b* in the diagram opposite.

(not to scale)

40°

60°

25° *a* *b*

....

....

2. Find angles *c*, *d* and *e* in the following diagram.

(not to scale)

c

40°

e

d

....

....

3. Look at the diagram opposite.

(not to scale)

B

E

24°

80°

D   C   A

Find:

(a) ∠ACB ....

(b) ∠DCE ....

(c) ∠DEC ....

4. Work out the values of *x*, *y* and *z* in the diagram opposite.

40° *y*

130°

100°

x

30°

z

(not to scale)

....

....

....

Geometry

1 In the diagram, which is not drawn to scale, the straight lines ABG and DEF are parallel. The straight lines BEC and GF are also parallel.

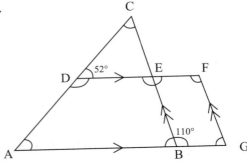

Find the following angles:

(a) ∠AGF ....

(b) ∠DEB ....

(c) ∠ACB ....

(d) ∠CAG ....

2 This diagram is not drawn to scale. AB is parallel to ED.

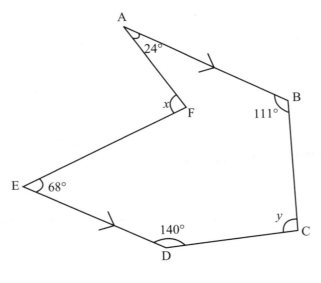

(a) Draw a line through F which is also parallel to AB and ED.

(b) Calculate x.

....

....

....

....

(c) Find y.

....

Circle Geometry

1 BD is a diameter of this circle and BC = CD. The diagram is not drawn to scale.

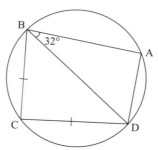

(a) Explain why ∠ADB = 58°.

....

(b) Find ∠ADC.

....

....

2 ABC is a tangent to this circle with centre O. It has not been drawn to scale.

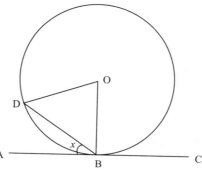

(a) State, giving a brief reason, angle OBC.

....

(b) Show that angle DOB is twice angle *x*.

....

....

....

Similarity

1   Look at these four shapes and complete the sentences below:

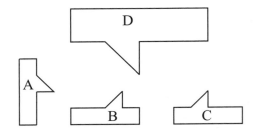

(a) Shapes ….. and ….. are congruent.

(b) Shapes ….. , ….. and ….. are similar.

2   This diagram shows two models of the same rocket.

(a) The smaller model is 57 cm tall. Find the height of the larger model.

....

(b) The fuselage is 12 cm wide on the larger model.
     Find the width of the fuselage on the smaller model.

....

(c) The angle of the nose cone on the smaller model is 42°.
     Find x, the angle of the nose cone on the larger model.

....

Enlargement

1   Phyllis has a photograph with an area of 16.4 cm².
    Phyllis's mother orders an enlargement by a scale factor of 3.
    Find the area of the enlargement.

    ....

2   A spherical iron cannonball, 10 cm wide, weighs 10 lb.
    Find the weight of a spherical iron cannonball 20 cm wide.

    ....

    ....

3   Enlarge this shape by a factor of 2 about the centre of enlargement (4, 1).

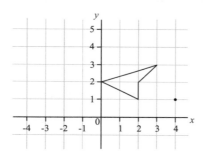

4   Quadrilateral B is an enlargement of quadrilateral A.

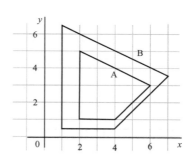

    (a) Find the scale factor of the enlargement.

    ....

    (b) Find the coordinates of the centre of the enlargement.

         Centre = (.... , ...)

    (c) A has an area of 10 cm². Calculate the area of B.

    ....

Translation

1 The diagram shows four triangles A, B, C and D on a coordinate grid.

Describe the translations which will map:

(a) A to B ....

(b) D to A ....

(c) A to C ....

(d) C to A ....

(e) B to C ....

(f) B to D ....

2 Here is a coordinate grid.

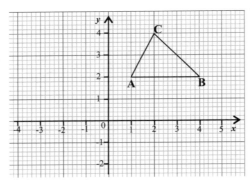

(a) Translate triangle ABC using vector $\begin{pmatrix} -5 \\ -1 \end{pmatrix}$.

Label the image $A_1B_1C_1$.

(b) Translate triangle $A_1B_1C_1$ onto $A_2B_2C_2$ using vector $\begin{pmatrix} 6 \\ -2 \end{pmatrix}$.

(c) Give the translation vector which translates the image of ABC onto $A_2B_2C_2$.

....

(d) What is the connection between the vectors in parts (a) and (b) and your answer to part (c)?

....

Rotation

1   T, the shaded triangle, has been rotated to form T_1 and T_2.

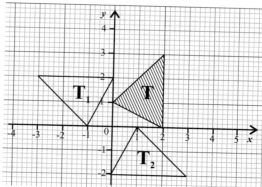

Describe fully the rotation:

(a) T to T_1. ....
....

(b) for which T_2 is the image of T. ....
....

(c) which maps T_2 to T_1. ....
....

2   Two triangles A and B have been drawn on this coordinate grid:

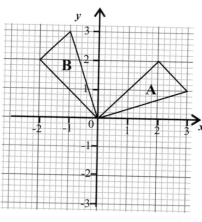

(a) Rotate A through 90° clockwise about the origin. Label the image A_1.

(b) Rotate B through 90° anticlockwise about the origin. Label the result B_1.

(c) Describe the transformation:

   (i)   which maps B_1 onto A_1 ....

   (ii) for which B is the image of A_1 ....

(d) Describe the symmetry of the whole diagram, ignoring the axes and labels.

....

Reflection

1 Look carefully at the five trapeziums drawn on this coordinate grid.

(a) State the mirror lines for the following reflections:

(i) A to B: ....

(ii) A to C: ....

(iii) C to E: ....

(b) Describe completely the transformation which will map C onto B. (It is not a reflection.)

....

....

2 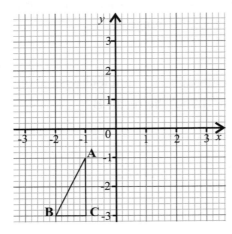 Triangle ABC has been drawn on this coordinate grid.

(a) Draw the reflection of ABC in the *x*-axis, and label the image $A_1B_1C_1$.

(b) Reflect $A_1B_1C_1$ in the *y*-axis. Label the image $A_2B_2C_2$.

(c) Now reflect $A_2B_2C_2$ in the line $y = x$ and label the image $A_3B_3C_3$.

(d) Describe in full the single transformation for which $A_3B_3C_3$ is the image of ABC.

....

....

Pythagoras' Theorem

1   Below are two right-angled triangles.

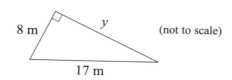

12 m, 16 m, x

8 m, 17 m, y (not to scale)

Calculate the lengths of the sides x and y.

....

....

2 A 10 m ladder, standing on horizontal ground, is leaning against a vertical wall.
The base of the ladder is 3 m from the wall.
How far up the wall will the ladder reach? Give your answer to 3 significant figures.

....

....

3   AB is a diameter of a circle with radius 9 cm. The chord AC = 6.2 cm.

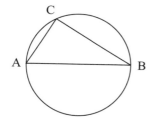

(a) Explain why you can use Pythagoras' theorem in triangle ABC.

....

....

(b) Find BC to three significant figures.

....

4 A triangle has sides of 37 cm, 37 cm and 24 cm.

Find its area.

....

....

....

Bearings

1 A gang of pirates start at Littleton and walk 3 km on a bearing of 105°. They then stop and bury their treasure. After burying their treasure they walk to Butterville.

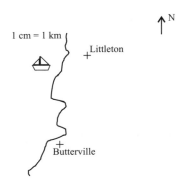

(a) On the map mark the point T where the treasure was buried.

(b) What was the bearing the pirates walked on to Butterville?

....

(c) How far is the treasure from Butterville?

....

2 The diagram shows a map of a desert.

½ cm = 1 km

↑ **N**

•Oasis

•
Camels

A tent can be found 5 km from the oasis on a bearing of 130°.

(a) Mark and label the tent on the diagram.

(b) On which bearing do the camels need to walk in order to reach the oasis?

....

....

Trigonometry

1 A tent is 1.5 m tall. It is anchored to the ground by guy ropes 2.6 m long.

(not to scale)

2.6 m

1.5 m

x

Find the angle, x, between the guy rope and the ground.

....

....

2 A tree is 240 cm tall. Its shadow is 670 cm long. x is the angle of elevation of the Sun.

(not to scale)

240 cm

670 cm

x

Work out the angle x to the nearest degree.

....

....

3 A cycle track on the sea wall is 3 m from the ground. A ramp is to be constructed between the ground and the cycle track on the sea wall. The angle of elevation of the ramp is to be 15°.

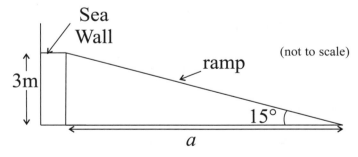

Sea Wall

ramp

(not to scale)

3m

15°

a

(a) Find a, the distance from the bottom of the ramp to the bottom of the sea wall.

....

(b) How long is the ramp?

....

Trigonometry

1 Mr Parker wants to work out the length of felt he needs to cover the roof of his shed.
The angle of elevation of the shed roof is 47°. The width of the shed is 3 m.

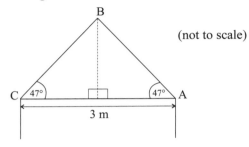

(not to scale)

(a) Work out BC, the length of felt needed to cover one side of the roof.

....

(b) Calculate the length of felt needed to cover the whole roof.

....

2 The design on a rectangular rug is made up of triangles.

(a) Calculate the size of angle θ.

....

(b) Calculate the length to the nearest cm of line r.

....

3 The diagram shows a church with a steeple.

(not to scale)   Find the distance from the ground to the top of the steeple
of the angle of elevation of the top of the steeple is 55°
from a point 9 m from the bottom of the church.

....

....

Loci and Constructions

1 ABCDE is the outline of planet Zing's flag.

The design on the flag is made by drawing all the points that are 2 cm from the line FG and then by drawing a line which is equidistant from ED and DC.

Complete the flag.

2 A, B, C and D are the corners of Mrs Jones' garden. There is a flower bed that is 2 m wide along the entire length of BC (7 m). There is also a patio in the shape of a sector of a circle with centre D and a radius of 3 m. The patio touches both AD and CD.

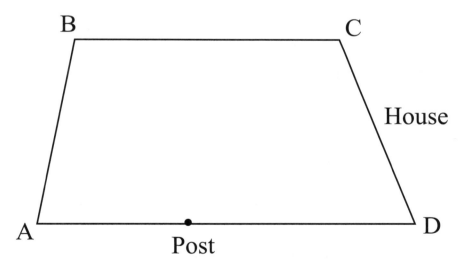

(a) On the diagram draw and label the flower bed.

(b) Draw and label the patio.

(c) Mrs Jones' son John has a goat chained to a post on AD.
The goat's chain just prevents him from stepping onto the flower bed and the patio.
Mark on the diagram the area where the goat can go.

Shapes Extra Practice (1)

1   Shape F is reflected in the *y*-axis and is then translated by vector $\begin{pmatrix} 2 \\ -5 \end{pmatrix}$.

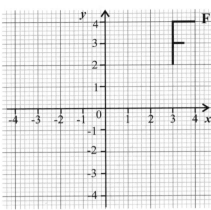

(a) Draw the reflection of shape F in the *y*-axis and label it F_1.

(b) Complete the transformation and label the final position of the shape F_2.

2   ABCDE is a pentagon made up of a parallelogram and a triangle.
BF = 4 cm, EG = 3 cm, and BC = 6 cm.

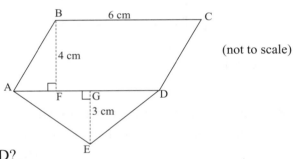

(not to scale)

(a) What is the area of the parallelogram ABCD?

....

(b) What is the area of the triangle ADE?

....

(c) What is the area of the pentagon ABCDE?

....

3   ABCDE is a regular pentagon. AB measures 8 cm.
Find:

(a) the perimeter of the pentagon. ....

(b) the exterior angle DEF. ....

(c) the interior angle EDC. ....

Shapes Extra Practice (1)

4 Add five more triangles to make this shape have rotational symmetry of order 4.

5 A wind farm is to be built off the coast. The windmills need to be at least 6 miles from the road linking Coral Bay to Digsworth. They must be closer to Digsworth than Coral Bay.

(a) Mark on the diagram a line 6 miles from the road.

(b) Complete the diagram by shading the area where the windmills may be erected.

6 A, B, C and D are points on a circle with centre O. Line EF touches the circle at D. Angle CDF = 35°.

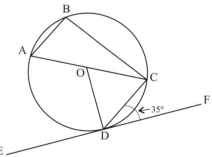

Find the size of the following angles.

(a) ∠ABC ....

(b) ∠OCD ....

(c) ∠COD ....

Shapes Extra Practice (1)

7 The diagram shows four lines. Two of the lines are parallel.

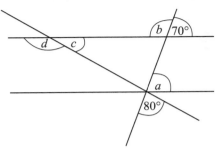

Work out the following angles:

(a) $a =$ ....

(b) $b =$ ....

(c) $c =$ ....

(d) $d =$ ....

8 The diagram shows a net of a solid object.

			F	
B	C	D	E	
A				

(a) Which shape is it a net of?

....

(b) The net is to be changed into the net of a pentagonal prism.

(i) Which shapes need to replace shapes A and F?

....

(ii) What else needs to be added?

....

9 Write L, A or V after each expression to show whether it represents a length, area or volume.
c, d, e, p, q, r, s, t are all lengths.

$4rst + t^3$ .... $2rd + 4st + 5qp$ .... $d + 2e + 4c$ ....

$2s^2 + 3dt$ .... $3p(r^2 + st)$ ....

Shapes Extra Practice (2)

1 The design on a jewellery box lid is shown in the diagram.

12 cm

θ

20 cm

(not to scale)

To make the design, wood needs to be cut at an angle of θ.
Using the measurements shown in the diagram, work out angle θ.

....

....

2 The diagram shows a solid whose uniform cross-section is a semicircle with a radius of 6 cm.

6 cm   15 cm

(a) Taking $\pi = 3.14$, find the area of the semicircle.

....

(b) Find the volume of the solid.

....

3 The diagram shows a child's sailing boat. The sails are triangular and angle ABC is a right angle. AB is 50 cm long and BC measures 30 cm.

A

50 cm

(not to scale)

B   30 cm   C

Work out the length of AC.

....

Probability

1   The probability that the school bus **is not** on time is 0.05.
    What is the probability that the bus **is** on time?

    ....

2   There are 18 balls in a bag. The bag contains blue, red and green balls.
    The probability of picking a blue ball is $\frac{1}{8}$ and the probability of picking a red ball is ¼.
    What is the probability of picking a green ball?

    ....

3   Two scratchcards, **A** and **B**, offer exactly the same prizes.
    The probability of winning a prize on scratchcard **A** is $\frac{1}{3}$.
    The probability of winning a prize on scratchcard **B** is $\frac{2}{5}$.
    Which one would you advise someone to buy? Explain why.

    ....

    ....

4   James has 8 chocolates left in a box. The chocolates are either hard or soft centred.

    (a) James picks a chocolate at random. If the probability of picking a soft centred chocolate is $\frac{3}{8}$,
        what is the probability he picks a hard centre?

        ....

    (b) James picks a hard centre and is disappointed. He puts it back without eating it and picks
        another chocolate. What is the probability that he chooses a soft centre now?

        ....

    (c) Assume that James has already taken one soft centred chocolate.
        What is the probability that he picks another soft centred chocolate?

        ....

Probability

1 List all the different three-course meals you could have from this menu.

Menu

Starter
Soup or Melon

Second Course
Lasagne, Fish or Chicken

Dessert
Ice-cream or Trifle

....

....

....

2 Using a fair dice, you have a $\frac{1}{6}$ chance of throwing each number.

(a) A fair dice is thrown once. What is the probability of scoring 3 or more?

....

(b) Two fair dice are thrown. One dice is green and the other red. What is the probability of
rolling an even number on the green dice and an odd number on the red dice at the same time?

....

3 Stewart's cash card lets him draw money from the cash machine at the bank.
The card has a four-figure PIN code number. Stewart has forgotten his code.
Stewart knows that the digits are 2, 4, 7 and 9. He also knows that the code
starts with a 7 and ends with an even digit.

(a) List all the possible code numbers that Stewart might try.

....

(b) The machine allows three attempts at getting it right before keeping the card.
What is the probability that Stewart will be able to get some money from the machine?

....

Estimating Probability

1 When rolling a fair dice, you have an equal chance of getting each number.

(a) What is the theoretical probability of rolling a fair dice and getting a 6?

....

(b) A fair dice is rolled 600 times. How many times would you expect it to land on a 6?

....

2 A coin is tossed 1000 times. It landed on heads 350 times.
Would you consider this to be a fair coin? Explain why.

....

....

3 This question is about estimated probability.

(a) In one 30-day month, Karen made her own bed 6 times.
What is the estimated probability that Karen will make her bed on a given day?

....

(b) Karen's brother Samson made his bed 15 times over a 90-day period.
What is the estimated probability that he will make his bed on a given day?

....

(c) In a 120-day period, how many times would you expect Karen to make her bed?

....

Combined Probability

1   State whether these pairs of events are **mutually exclusive** or **independent**.

(a) Drawing an ace from a pack of cards and tossing heads on a coin.

....

(b) Throwing a dice once and getting an even number and an odd number.

....

2   Calculate the probability of the following:

(a) Throwing a 3 or a 4 with a dice.

....

(b) Drawing a heart from a pack of cards, replacing it and then drawing a spade.

....

(c) Drawing a king from a pack of cards (not replacing it) and then drawing an ace.

....

3   The probability that Natalia will beat Ahmed at a computer game is 0.65.
They play two games.

(a) Calculate the probability that Natalia wins both games.

....

(b) Calculate the probability that Natalia loses both games.

....

(c) Calculate the probability that they win a game each.

....

Probability — Tree Diagrams

1 The probability that it will rain on any one day is 0.4.

(a) Complete the tree diagram below, showing the possible outcomes.

R = rain
N = not rain

	1st day	2nd day	Outcome	Probability

0.4 R

0.4 R

R

0.6 N

(R, R) $0.4 \times 0.4 = 0.16$

....

0.6

0.4 R

N

0.6 N

....

....

(b) What is the probability that it will rain on at least one day?

....

2 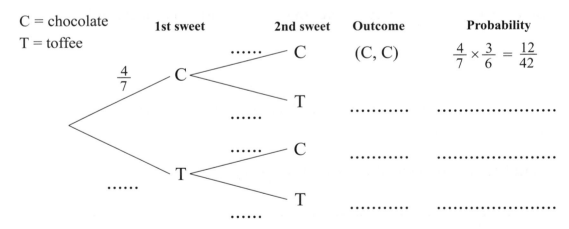 A bag of sweets contains 4 chocolates and 3 toffees.
Two sweets are taken out at random and eaten.

(a) Complete the tree diagram to show the possible outcomes.

C = chocolate
T = toffee

	1st sweet	2nd sweet	Outcome	Probability

...... C

$\frac{4}{7}$ C

T
......

(C, C) $\frac{4}{7} \times \frac{3}{6} = \frac{12}{42}$

....

...... C

T
......

T

......

....

....

(b) Calculate the probability of choosing one of each type of sweet.

....

(c) Calculate the probability of choosing the same type of sweet twice.

....

Graphs and Charts

1 The table shows the marks for ten pupils in their Maths and French examinations.

Pupil	Sinead	Clare	Andy	Pedro	Beth	Curtis	Kyle	Molly	Sam	Anita
Maths	26	21	32	30	38	41	39	43	15	26
French	25	26	25	29	30	37	32	44	13	20

(a) Plot the data on a scatter diagram. Use the graph below.

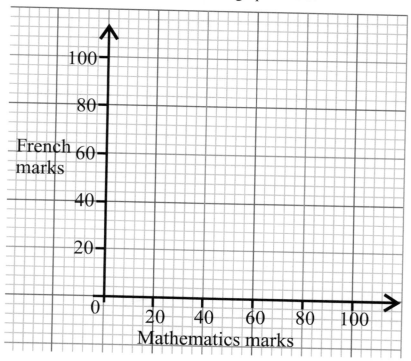

(b) Draw the line of best fit.

(c) Describe the type of correlation this data shows.

....

(d) A pupil was absent for the French exam but scored 28 in the Maths exam.
   What mark would you expect him to have got in French?

....

(e) Another pupil was absent for the Maths exam but scored 37 in French.
   What mark would you expect her to have got in Maths?

....

Graphs and Charts

1 45 pupils were asked where they went last year for their summer holiday.
Their responses were organised into this frequency table.

Destination	Frequency	Angle of sector (°)
UK and Ireland	12	
Spain	15	
France	8	
USA	6	
Other	4	

(a) You are going to draw a pie chart using this information.
Calculate the angle of the sector for each destination and add it to the table above.

....

....

....

....

(b) Draw and label a pie chart
of this information.

2 A group of teenagers were asked what their favourite weekend pastime was.
A pie chart was drawn to represent their responses. 20 teenagers said their favourite
pastime was going to the cinema. The angle of this sector is calculated to be 40°.

How many teenagers took part in the survey?

....

....

Mean, Median, Mode and Range

1 15 students were asked how many text messages they had sent the previous day.
These were their responses:

20 18 3 5 15 11 3 9 8 12 22 4 9 12 9

Calculate the following:

(a) median ....

....

(b) mode ....

(c) range ....

2 Here are the amounts which four teenagers spent at the weekend:

£100, £12, £4, £4

(a) Calculate the mean, median and mode for this data.

mean ....

median ....

mode ....

(b) Which of these averages is the best one to use to represent average weekend expenditure?
Give a reason for your answer.

....

....

3 Dan is a member of a pub quiz team. His team have played three games.
In the first game they scored 25 points and in the second they scored 32 points.
Their mean score for the three games was 30 points.
How many points did Dan's team score in the third game?

....

....

Frequency Tables

1 A survey of the number of TVs in pupils' homes gave these results.

Number of TVs	Frequency	Number of TVs × Frequency
1	55	55
2	68	136
3	75	
4	25	
5	15	
6	8	
7	4	
TOTALS		

(a) Complete the frequency table.

(b) How many pupils took part in the survey?

....

(c) Calculate the mean number of TVs.

....

(d) What was the modal number of TVs in pupils' homes? ....

(e) Calculate the median number of TVs in pupils' homes.

....

....

(f) Calculate the range for this data. ....

Grouped Frequency Tables

1 The table shows the ages of 300 people at the cinema.

Age in years	Frequency (f)	Mid-Interval Value (x)	f × x
15 to 19	125		
20 to 24	85		
25 to 29	40		
30 to 34	35		
35 to 39	15		
TOTALS	300	—	

(a) Complete the table above and use the information to calculate an estimate of the mean age.

....

(b) What is the modal age?

....

(c) Calculate the median age group.

....

2 50 pupils in Year 9 were asked how much TV they usually watched in an evening.
The results were grouped in a frequency table.

Time spent watching TV (minutes)	Frequency
$0 \leq$ time < 60	7
$60 \leq$ time < 120	12
$120 \leq$ time < 180	22
$180 \leq$ time < 240	9
TOTAL	50

Show that an estimate of the mean time spent watching TV in an evening is 129.6 minutes.

....

....

....

Cumulative Frequency Tables

1 100 students were asked how much they had spent on their school lunch that day.
The data was arranged in a cumulative frequency table.
Complete the missing values in the table.

Expenditure in pence (x)	Frequency	Cumulative Frequency
$0 \leq x < 50$	2	
$50 \leq x < 100$	2	
$100 \leq x < 150$		22
$150 \leq x < 200$		76
$200 \leq x < 250$	10	
$250 \leq x < 300$		100

2 The heights of a class of Year 9 pupils were recorded to the nearest centimetre.
These are the results.

162, 185, 177, 165, 155, 162, 153, 160, 180, 162, 141, 147, 155, 161,
159, 170, 162, 167, 150, 166, 142, 169, 143, 152, 179, 158, 177

(a) Organise the results in the grouped frequency table below.

Heights in cm (h)	Tally	Frequency	Cumulative Frequency
$140 \leq h < 150$			
$150 \leq h < 160$			
$160 \leq h < 170$			
$170 \leq h < 180$			
$180 \leq h < 190$			

(b) From the table, calculate which group contains the median height.

....

....

Cumulative Frequency Curves

1 Use the data in question 2 on page 90 for this question.

(a) Draw a cumulative frequency curve of the data on the grid below.

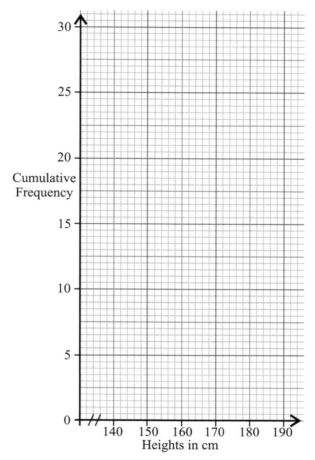

(b) Use your graph to find the following:

(i) the median height .... (ii) the lower quartile ....

(iii) the upper quartile .... (iv) the interquartile range ....

(c) Use your graph to estimate how many pupils had a height of 164 cm or less.

....

(d) Use your graph to estimate how many pupils had a height of 177 cm or more.

....

Statistics & Probability Extra Practice (1)

1. There are some counters in a bag. The counters are either blue or green.
If you take a counter at random out of the bag, the probability that it will be green is ¼.

   (a) What is the probability that the counter will be blue? ....

   (b) A pupil takes one counter out of the bag. It is green.
   What is the smallest number of blue counters there could be in the bag?

   ....

   (c) Then the pupil takes another counter out of the bag. It is also green. Using this new information, what is the smallest number of blue counters there could be in the bag?

   ....

   (d) A different bag has red, yellow and pink counters in it. There are 20 counters in the bag and at least one of each of the three colours. If you take a counter out of the bag at random, the probability that it will be yellow is $\frac{2}{5}$. What is the greatest number of pink counters there could be in the bag?

   ....

   ....

2. Nestor achieved a mean score of 20 in a total of 3 games.
The score for each game is given by the following expressions:

Game 1:	$3x + 10$
Game 2:	$2x + 5$
Game 3:	$x - 3$

   Calculate the value of x and work out the points he scored in each game.

   ....

   ....

   ....

   ....

Statistics & Probability Extra Practice (1)

3 A class collected information about the number of pets in each of their families.
This information was displayed in a frequency table.

Number of Pets	Number of Families
0	4
1	6
2	8
3	n
4	1

The value for the number of families that said they had 3 pets is missing. It has been replaced with the letter n.

(a) Show that the total number of pets in all the families is $26 + 3n$.

....

....

(b) Write an expression for the total number of families.

....

(c) The mean number of pets per family is 2. What is the value of n?

....

....

4 A greengrocer recorded the weight of each
watermelon sold in the summer season.
Draw a frequency polygon to show the
weights of the melons sold.

Weight in kg (W)	Frequency
$0.5 \leq W < 1$	22
$1 \leq W < 1.5$	36
$1.5 \leq W < 2$	15
$2 \leq W < 2.5$	19
$2.5 \leq W < 3$	8
TOTAL	100

Statistics & Probability Extra Practice (2)

1 Rina makes two wooden mirrors. Each mirror is hand-crafted independently.
The probability that the wood splits whilst being crafted is 0.06.

(a) Calculate the probability that both of Rina's wooden mirrors split whilst being crafted.

....

(b) Calculate the probability that only one of Rina's mirrors splits whilst being crafted.

....

....

(c) Rina has enough wood to make 60 mirrors. She receives an order for 55 mirrors.
Is she likely to have enough wood to make all 55 mirrors without splits? Explain your answer.

....

....

2 The number of days 280 pupils were absent for during a year was recorded in a frequency table.

Number of days absent	Frequency (f)	Cumulative Frequency	Midpoint (x)	$f \times x$
0 to 4	32			
5 to 9	67			
10 to 14	131			
15 to 19	43			
20 to 24	7			

(a) Calculate the midpoint for each class interval and enter it in the table.

(b) Complete the cumulative frequency column and use it to help find the median.

....

(c) Complete the table and calculate an estimate of the mean for this data.

....

KS3

Mathematics

Topic-based Practice Questions

Answer Book

Levels 5-8

Contents

SECTION ONE — NUMBERS MOSTLY 3

SECTION TWO — ALGEBRA 5

SECTION THREE — SHAPES 10

SECTION FOUR — STATISTICS & PROBABILITY 14

Published by Coordination Group Publications Ltd

ISBN: 978 1 84146 526 5
Groovy website: www.cgpbooks.co.uk
Printed by Elanders Hindson Ltd, Newcastle upon Tyne.

Section One — Numbers Mostly

Page 1

1 (a) (i) 24 and 1; 12 and 2; 8 and 3; 6 and 4

 (ii) 1, 2, 3, 4, 6, 8, 12, 24

 (b) 1, 2, 3, 4, 6, 9, 12, 18, 36

2 (a) 18   (b) 24

3 (a)

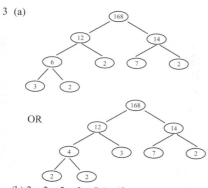

 OR

 (b) $2 \times 2 \times 2 \times 3 \times 7$ ($= 2^3 \times 3 \times 7$)

 Make sure you can write large numbers as products of prime factors —
 it's one of those things that comes up in tests all the time.

Page 2

1 (a) 22: 1, 2, 11, 22

   41: 1, 41

   33: 1, 3, 11, 33

   62: 1, 2, 31, 62

 (b) 41   (c) It is the only one with only two factors.

   Remember — a prime number can only be divided by itself and one.

2   2

3

4 (a) T   (b) F   (c) T   (d) F

Page 3

1 (a) and (b)

⊗	2	③	✖	5	⑥	7	8	✖	⑩
11	12	13	14	⑮	✖	17	18	19	20
㉑	22	23	24	✖	26	27	㉘	29	30
31	32	33	34	35	⊗	37	38	39	40

 (c) 1, 36

2   Odd: $3Y$, $X-7$, $\dfrac{X}{X}$

   Even: $Y-1$, $6Y$, XY, X^2

   For questions like these, try putting in simple values for X and Y. If it comes out as odd
   *for **one** even number, it'll be odd for **all** even numbers, and vice versa.*

3   An odd number greater than 100 — 27

   An even square number — 28

   A triangular number — 144

   An odd cube number — 121

Page 4

1 (a) $\dfrac{5}{15} = \dfrac{6}{18} = \dfrac{7}{21}$ (The numerator increases by 1 each time, the denominator by 3.) Fraction in its simplest form: $\dfrac{1}{3}$

 (b) $\dfrac{15}{25} = \dfrac{18}{30} = \dfrac{21}{35}$ (The numerator increases by 3, the denominator by 5.)

   Fraction in its simplest form: $\dfrac{3}{5}$

   Don't throw away marks on easy questions like these.

2 (a) $5 \times 2 = 10$ so $5 \times 9 = a = \mathbf{45}$

 (b) $8 \times 7 = 56$ so $8b = 24$ so $b = \mathbf{3}$

 (c) $8 \times 9 = 72$ so $8 \times 8 = c = \mathbf{64}$

3

Simplified Fraction	Fraction out of one hundred	Percentage
$\frac{1}{2}$	$\frac{50}{100}$	**50**
$\frac{7}{10}$	$\frac{70}{100}$	70
$\frac{19}{20}$	$\frac{95}{100}$	**95**
$\frac{8}{25}$	$\frac{32}{100}$	**32**
$\frac{3}{50}$	$\frac{6}{100}$	6

4 (a) To get from $2a$ to $8ab$, you need to multiply by $4b$.

   Missing term $= \dfrac{20b}{4b} = \mathbf{5}$

 (b) To get from $3x$ to $6xy$, you need to multiply by $2y$.

   Missing term $= 2y \times 5x^2 = \mathbf{10x^2y}$

   Cancelling down equations should feel like second nature now.

Page 5

1   $\dfrac{1}{20}$, 9%, 0.12, $\dfrac{13}{100}$, 17%, $\dfrac{9}{50}$

2 (a) $\dfrac{2}{5} = \dfrac{40}{100} = \mathbf{40\%}$ (b) $\dfrac{17}{20} = \dfrac{85}{100} = \mathbf{85\%}$ (c) $x\%$

3 (a) No, Lydia is not right.

 (b) Either because $\dfrac{1}{8}$ is 0.125 (not 0.8), or because 0.8 is $\dfrac{4}{5}$ (not $\dfrac{1}{8}$).

4

Fraction	Decimal	Percentage
$\frac{19}{100}$	0.19	19
$\frac{3}{8} \left(\frac{375}{1000}\right)$	0.375	37.5
$\frac{1}{25} \left(\frac{4}{100}\right)$	0.04	4
$\frac{41}{50} \left(\frac{82}{100}\right)$	0.82	82
$\frac{11}{16}$	0.6875	68.75

 Remember — percentages are fractions that are out of a hundred, so it's easy to
 convert between the two.

Page 6

1 (a) 0.077

 (b) 0.08

2   52200, 51520

   Sig figs come up in all sorts of different questions, so it's worth learning them.

3

	1 sig. fig.	2 sig. figs	3 sig. figs
5653	**6000**	**5700**	**5650**
42.56	**40**	**43**	**42.6**
0.3592	**0.4**	**0.36**	**0.359**
9.995	**10**	**10**	**10.0**
0.001596	**0.002**	**0.0016**	**0.00160**

4 (a) $19.5 \times 15.5 = \mathbf{302.25\ m^2}$

 (b) $20.5 + 20.5 + 16.5 + 16.5 = \mathbf{74\ m}$

Page 7

1   $5.863\ m \times 3.67\ m = 21.51721\ m^2$, so either **21.5 m²** or **22 m²**

2 (a) 1.63 m

 (b) 53 litres

 (c) 50 000 000 miles

4

3   614 is approximately 600. 154 is approximately 150. $\dfrac{600}{150}=\mathbf{4}$

No, Harry is not right.

Something tells me Harry was trying to pull a swift one.

4 $\dfrac{5\times40}{300+100}=\dfrac{200}{400}=\mathbf{\dfrac{1}{2}}$

Page 8

1 (a) 3 mins 52 secs $=3\frac{52}{60}$ mins $=3.867$ mins, so **3.83 mins** is a faster time than 3 mins 52 secs.

(b) $3.867-3.83=0.037$. To convert this into seconds, multiply by 60, which gives **2.22 secs**.

2 (a) $\dfrac{6000\ m}{50\ 000}=0.12\ m=\mathbf{12\ cm}$ (b) $0.32\ m\times50\ 000=16\ 000\ m=\mathbf{16\ km}$

3 (a) $500\times1.63=\mathbf{€815}$

(b) $\dfrac{142}{1.63}=\mathbf{£87.12}$ (c) $\dfrac{73}{1.49}=£48.99\approx\mathbf{£49}$

*In questions like this, always bear in mind that a given amount will be **more euros than pounds**. That should help you to get the conversion right.*

Page 9

1

42 mm	**4.2 cm**
2450 m	**2.45 km**
392 cm	**3.92 m**
2.93 km	**2930 m**
0.08 cm	**0.8 mm**

2

	Metric Unit	Imperial Unit
Amount of water in a bath	**Litre**	**Gallon**
Height of a doorway	**Metre / Centimetre**	**Foot / Inch**
One bag of sugar	**Kilogram / Gram**	**Pound**
Length of a pencil	**Centimetre**	**Inch**
Distance from London to Glasgow	**Kilometre**	**Mile**

3 (a) 1 kg = 2.2 lb. $\dfrac{27}{2.2}=\mathbf{12.27\ kg}$

(b) 1 stone = 14 lb. 2 stone 3 lb = 31 lb. $\dfrac{31}{2.2}=\mathbf{14.09\ kg}$.

14.09 + 12.27 = **26.36 kg**

It's useful to have some idea about metric and imperial units. It may stop you getting bamboozled in shops too.

Page 10

1

Decimal	Fraction
0.7	$\frac{7}{10}$
0.23	$\frac{23}{100}$
0.096	$\frac{12}{125}\ \left(\frac{96}{1000}\right)$
0.08	$\frac{2}{25}\ \left(\frac{8}{100}\right)$
1.925	$1\frac{37}{40}\ \left(\frac{1925}{1000}\right)$

2 (a) $\dfrac{4}{5}$ (b) $\dfrac{3}{7}$

3 (a) $\dfrac{2\times4}{3\times11}=\mathbf{\dfrac{8}{33}}$ (b) $\dfrac{5}{8}\times\dfrac{3}{2}=\mathbf{\dfrac{15}{16}}$

When you're dividing fractions, flip over the second fraction and multiply.

4 (a) $£5.00\times\dfrac{3}{10}=\dfrac{£15.00}{10}=\mathbf{£1.50}$

(b) Sweets: £1.50

Magazines: $£5.00\times\dfrac{1}{4}=\dfrac{£5.00}{4}=£1.25$

Toys: $£5.00\times\dfrac{2}{5}=\dfrac{£5.00\times2}{5}=£2.00$

$£1.50+£1.25+£2.00=£4.75$

$£5.00-£4.75=\mathbf{£0.25}$

Page 11

1 (a) $\dfrac{3}{8}$, 0.375   (b) $\dfrac{14}{15}$, 0.9333   (c) $\dfrac{14}{3}$ or $4\frac{2}{3}$, 4.6667

If you want to know if a number is divisible by 3, find the sum of the digits. If this is in the 3 times table, the number is divisible by 3.

2 $\dfrac{23}{7}=3.286$ and $2\frac{3}{7}=2.429$

3 (a) $3\dfrac{5}{8}+1\dfrac{7}{16}=3\dfrac{10}{16}+1\dfrac{7}{16}=\mathbf{5\dfrac{1}{16}}$

(b) $\dfrac{9}{10}\times1\dfrac{11}{12}=\dfrac{9}{10}\times\dfrac{23}{12}=\dfrac{207}{120}=\dfrac{69}{40}=\mathbf{1\dfrac{29}{40}}$

(c) $2\dfrac{5}{12}\div\dfrac{29}{24}=\dfrac{29}{12}\div\dfrac{29}{24}=\dfrac{29}{12}\times\dfrac{24}{29}=\dfrac{24}{12}=\mathbf{2}$

4 (a) To get from 25 to 5, you need to divide by 5, so $x=5\times14=\mathbf{70}$.

(b) $4\dfrac{1}{2}=\dfrac{9}{2}$, so $x=\mathbf{2}$

(c) To get from 8 to 4, you need to divide by 2, so $\dfrac{3x}{2}=3$, $x=\mathbf{2}$.

Page 12

1 (a) $\dfrac{39}{100}\times300=39\times\dfrac{300}{100}=39\times3=\mathbf{£117}$

(b) $\dfrac{20}{100}\times14.20=\dfrac{2\times14.2}{10}=\dfrac{28.4}{10}=\mathbf{£2.84}$

(c) $\dfrac{84}{100}\times2.50=84\times\dfrac{2.5}{100}=84\times\dfrac{1}{40}=\dfrac{21}{10}=\mathbf{£2.10}$

2   Maths: $\dfrac{46}{60}\times100=\mathbf{76.7\%}$

English $\dfrac{75}{95}\times100=\mathbf{78.9\%}$

Science $\dfrac{27}{35}\times100=\mathbf{77.1\%}$

3 $£9450\times0.825=\mathbf{£7796.25}$

4 $£102\times0.1=£10.20$, so Mr Patel would be better off choosing 10%.

$£98.50\times0.1=£9.85$, so Miss Dalton would not be better off choosing 10%.

$£120\times0.1=£12$, so Mrs Ferrar would be better off choosing 10%.

Answer: **Mr Patel and Mrs Ferrar**

Page 13

1 (a) (i) $£4400-£4000=\mathbf{£400}$

(ii) $\dfrac{£400}{£4000}=\dfrac{1}{10}=\mathbf{10\%}$

(b) $£4000-£3500=£500$

$\dfrac{£500}{£4000}=\dfrac{1}{8}=\mathbf{12.5\%}$

2   Let the original price of the car be x.

$x-(15\%\ of\ x)=£1700$

85% of $x=£1700$

$\dfrac{85x}{100}=£1700$

$\dfrac{17x}{20}=£1700$

$\dfrac{x}{20}=£100$

$x=\mathbf{£2000}$

I find that making the original price 'x' means I'm less likely to make a cock-up of the whole question.

Let the original price of each bed be P.

Single Bed:
$$P \times 85\% = £65$$
$$0.85P = £65$$
$$P = \frac{£65}{0.85} = \mathbf{£76.47}$$

Double Bed:
$$P \times 65\% = £240$$
$$0.65P = £240$$
$$P = \frac{£240}{0.65} = \mathbf{£369.23}$$

Bunk Beds:
$$P \times 60\% = £190$$
$$0.6P = £190$$
$$P = \frac{£190}{0.6} = \mathbf{£316.67}$$

4 (a) $1.67 - 1.28 = 0.39$

$\frac{0.39}{1.28} = 0.30469 \approx \mathbf{30.5\%}$

(b) $\frac{0.30469}{2} = 0.15234$

$1.15234 \times 1.67 = \mathbf{1.92\ m}$

Page 14

1 (a) $3 : 8$　　(b) $1 : 3$　　(c) $6 : 7$　　(d) $10 : 7$

2 (a) $\frac{13}{5} = \mathbf{2.6\ times}$　　(b) Let there be 18 parts in total $(5 + 13)$.

$$\frac{144\ g}{18} = 8\ g$$
$$13 \times 8\ g = \mathbf{104\ g}$$

(c) $\frac{5}{13}$ g or 0.385 g

3 (a) $x + 2x + (x + 3) = 42$　　$4x + 3 = 42$　　$x = \frac{39}{4} = \mathbf{9.75\ W}$

(b) Mic C is at $9.75 + 3 = 12.75$ W　　$\frac{12.75\ W}{9.75\ W} = \mathbf{1.31\ times}$

Why doesn't 'ratio' rhyme with 'patio'?

Page 15

1 (a) 9.845×10^4　　(b) 8.3×10^0　　(c) 6.4×10^{-3}　　(d) 9.7×10^{-1}

2 (a) India　　(b) UK

(c) India: $\frac{1.0 \times 10^9}{3.3 \times 10^6} = \frac{1}{3.3} \times 10^3 = 303$ people per km^2.

UK: $\frac{6.0 \times 10^7}{2.4 \times 10^5} = \frac{6}{2.4} \times 10^2 = 250$ people per km^2.

So **53 more people per km²**.

3 (a) 5×10^{-4}　　(b) 5×10^{-5}

(c) $0.0005 + 0.00005 = 0.00055 = \mathbf{5.5 \times 10^{-4}}$

Putting very small or very large numbers into standard form makes them easier to work with. It saves you having to count all those noughts all the time.

Page 16

1 (a) $3^{4+2} = \mathbf{3^6}$　　(b) $5^{8-5} = \mathbf{5^3}$　　(c) $2^{6 \times 3} = \mathbf{2^{18}}$　　(d) 3^1

If your mind goes blank in a test and you forget all the rules about indices, go back to first principles. For example, you know that 3 times 3 equals 9, that's to say: $3^1 \times 3^1 = 3^2$. From this, you can see that: $x^y \times x^z = x^{y+z}$.

2 (a) $\frac{2^{2 \times 4} \times 2^3 \times 1^{65}}{2^0 \times 2^{3 \times 3}} = \frac{2^8 \times 2^3 \times 1}{1 \times 2^9} = \frac{2^{8+3}}{2^9} = \frac{2^{11}}{2^9} = 2^{11-9} = 2^2 = \mathbf{4}$

(b) $\frac{\left(\frac{3^{10}}{3^8}\right) \times (3^2)^5}{(3^2)^2 \times 3^4} = \frac{3^{10-8} \times 3^{2 \times 5}}{3^{2 \times 2} \times 3^4} = \frac{3^2 \times 3^{10}}{3^4 \times 3^4} = \frac{3^{2+10}}{3^{4+4}} = \frac{3^{12}}{3^8} = 3^{12-8} = 3^4 = \mathbf{81}$

3 (a) $729 = 9^3$ and $6561 = 9^4$.　　$9^3 \times 9^4 = 9^7 = 4\ 782\ 969$

(b) (i) $\frac{9^8}{9^6} = 9^2 = \mathbf{81}$　　(ii) $9^3 \times 9^2 = 9^5 = \mathbf{59\ 049}$

Page 17

1 (a) 5.22　　(b) 11.92　　(c) 9.06　　(d) 12.57

2 (a) $\sqrt[3]{400\ cm^3} = \mathbf{7.37\ cm}$　　(b) $\sqrt[3]{12\ 680\ m^3} = \mathbf{23.3\ m}$　　(c) $\sqrt[3]{12\ mm^3} = \mathbf{2.29\ mm}$

Don't throw marks away by getting the units wrong.

3 (a) Either 'the cube root of G squared' or 'the square of the cube root of G'.

(b) (i) 4　　(ii) 9　　(iii) 25

Pages 18 and 19

1 (a) $15 \times 4 = \mathbf{60}$　　(b) $60 \times 2 = \mathbf{120}$　　(c) $\frac{30}{2} \times 3 = \mathbf{45}$

2 35% of 60 = 21, 65% of 60 = 39. $(21 \times 2) + 39 = \mathbf{81\ lambs}$

3 (a) (i) 5^3　　(ii) 3^4　　(b) 2^5 and 2^7

4 (a) 10% of £30 + 5% of £30 = £3 + £1.50 = **£4.50**

(b) £6.75 = £2.25 + £4.50 = 5% + 10% of **£45**

(c) £10.50 = $(3 \times £3) + £1.50 = (3 \times 10\%) + 5\%$ of £30 = **35%** of £30

(d) 25p is half of 50p. Because 50p is 5% of £10, 25p must be 5% of half of £10, so 25p = 5% of **£5**.

5 (a) $\frac{72}{9} = \mathbf{8}$　　(b) $33 \times 0.5 \approx \mathbf{16}$　　(c) $\frac{10 + 20}{5} = \mathbf{6}$　　(d) $\frac{30 \times 24}{6 \times 4} = \frac{30 \times 24}{24} = \mathbf{30}$

6 (a) $g = 1$　　(b) $g = 24$

7 (a) 45　　(b) 41, 43, 47

Pages 20 and 21

1 (a) $\frac{5.93}{12.56} \times 100 = \mathbf{47.2\%}$

(b) $\frac{316.75}{430.50} \times 100 = \mathbf{73.6\%}$, compared to 47.2%, is a greater proportion.

Imagine earning £5.93 a week. Still, in those days, that'd buy you a 3-bedroomed semi, a Morris Minor and a weekend in Bognor.

2 (a) Saturn

(b) $V = \frac{4}{3} \times 3.142 \times (6.4 \times 10^6)^3 = \frac{4}{3} \times 3.142 \times (6.4^3 \times 10^{6 \times 3})$

$= \frac{4}{3} \times 3.142 \times 262.144 \times 10^{18} = 1098.209 \times 10^{18} = \mathbf{1.10 \times 10^{21}\ m^3}$

3 Let the original price of the shoes be x.

$x - (15\%\ of\ x) = £38.25$

85% of $x = £38.25$

$0.85x = £38.25$

$x = \frac{£38.25}{0.85} = \mathbf{£45}$

4 (a) $1.62 \times 1800 = \mathbf{\$2916}$　　(b) $\frac{126}{1.78} \times 0.9 = \mathbf{£63.71}$

5 $x = \sqrt{4.3^2 + 9.63^2} = \sqrt{111.2269} = \mathbf{10.55\ km}$

6 (a) $12 \times 4.5 = \mathbf{54\ litres}$　　(b) $\frac{192}{2.2} = \mathbf{87.3\ kg}$

(c) $\frac{1.83}{0.9} \times 36 = 73.2$ inches. $\frac{73.2}{12} = 6$ feet 1.2 inches, so **6 feet 1 inch**.

Take another good look at any questions you got wrong.
And get any problems sorted out sooner rather than later.

Section Two — Algebra

Page 22

1 (a) $3T - 17 = 28$　　(b) $D = 46 - 2T$

2 $1000 + 6x = 1648$ or $10 + 0.06x = 16.48$

$6x = 648$

$x = \mathbf{108\ calls}$

3 (a) $3 \times 24 = £72$

(b) $\frac{5x + 5x + 5x + 4.50 + 5.20 + 2.30}{3} = 24$ or $15x + 12 = 72$ or $\frac{15x + 12}{3} = 24$

(Other answers are also possible.)

    (c) $15x + 12 = 72$
       $15x = 60$
        $x = £4$

Page 23

1 (a) $7x - y$ (b) $6x^2 + 4x - 5 - x^3$ (c) $a + 3b + b^2 - 4ab$

2 (a) $10x - 2$ (b) $24x^2 - 18xy$ (c) $-16a^2 + 8ab$

    (d) $-6wx - 15wy$ (e) $6x^2y - xy^2$

3 (a) $P = 3x + 3x + x + 4 + x + 4 = \mathbf{8x + 8 \text{ or } 8(x + 1)}$

    (b) $A = 3x(x + 4) = \mathbf{3x^2 + 12x}$

      On this one, you've got to know that the area of a rectangle = length × width.
      Don't get it muddled up with perimeter, which is the distance around the edge.

Page 24

1 (a) $x^2 + 3x + 6x + 18 = \mathbf{x^2 + 9x + 18}$

    (b) $x^2 + 4x + 9x + 36 = \mathbf{x^2 + 13x + 36}$

    (c) $x^2 + 4x - 3x - 12 = \mathbf{x^2 + x - 12}$

    (d) $x^2 - 3x + 3x - 9 = \mathbf{x^2 - 9}$

    (e) $x^2 - 5x - 2x + 10 = \mathbf{x^2 - 7x + 10}$

2 (a) $2x^2 + x + 4x + 2 = \mathbf{2x^2 + 5x + 2}$

    (b) $6x^2 + 4x + 15x + 10 = \mathbf{6x^2 + 19x + 10}$

    (c) $2x^2 - 3x + 8x - 12 = \mathbf{2x^2 + 5x - 12}$

    (d) $4x^2 - 5x - 4x + 5 = \mathbf{4x^2 - 9x + 5}$

    (e) $4x^2 + 2x - 2x - 1 = \mathbf{4x^2 - 1}$

3 (a) David has forgotten the minus sign. $-1 \times 1 = -1$.
    It should be $3x^2 - x + 3x - 1 = 3x^2 + 2x - 1$.

    (b) David has added instead of multiplying.
    It should be $15x^2 + 10x + 9x + 6 = 15x^2 + 19x + 6$.

      Here's another handy tip — use the FOIL method when you expand out brackets.
      Multiply the first number in each bracket, the outside numbers, the inside numbers,
      then the last numbers in each bracket. Now just add all the like terms together.

Page 25

1 (a) $x^2 + 2x + 3x + 6 = \mathbf{x^2 + 5x + 6}$

    (b) $2x^2 - 12x - x + 6 = \mathbf{2x^2 - 13x + 6}$

    (c) $2a^2 + 4ab - ab - 2b^2 = \mathbf{2a^2 + 3ab - 2b^2}$

    (d) $2x^3 - 4x^2 + x - 2$

    (e) $221x^2 + 117x - 68x - 36 = \mathbf{221x^2 + 49x - 36}$

2 (a) $(x + 2)(x + 2) = x^2 + 2x + 2x + 4 = \mathbf{x^2 + 4x + 4}$

    (b) $(2a - b)(2a - b) = 4a^2 - 2ab - 2ab + b^2 = \mathbf{4a^2 - 4ab + b^2}$

    (c) $(25x - 6)(25x - 6) = 625x^2 - 150x - 150x + 36 = \mathbf{625x^2 - 300x + 36}$

3 (a) $(2x + 3)^2$

    (b) $(2x + 3)(2x + 3) = 4x^2 + 6x + 6x + 9 = \mathbf{4x^2 + 12x + 9}$

Page 26

1 (a) $2x(x - 2)$ (b) $xy(3y - 5x)$

   (c) $2b(4a - b + 5c)$ (d) $4(x - 2y)$

2 (a) $2y(3x - 5)$ (b) $6x - 10$ (or $2(3x - 5)$)

3 (a) $x^2 + 4x$ (b) $x(x + 4)$

Page 27

1 (a) 20, 23 (each number is 3 more than the last)

    (b) 70, 70 (the difference changes by 2 each time)

    (c) 0.001, 0.0001 (divide each number by 10 to get the next)

      This stuff should be easy marks. Make sure your rule works for the
      whole sequence though, not just for the first two numbers.

2 (a)

    (b) Black: 25 Grey: 24

3 (a) 1386, 2239 (each number is the sum of the previous two terms)

    (b) 635, 1275 (the difference doubles each time)

    (c) 1.65, 1.62 (subtract 0.03 each time)

Page 28

1 (a) $a = 2, d = 2$
    So n^{th} term $= dn + (a - d) = 2n + (2 - 2) = \mathbf{2n}$

    (b) $a = 1, d = 2$
    So n^{th} term $= dn + (a - d) = 2n + (1 - 2) = \mathbf{2n - 1}$

    (or you could have noticed the numbers are one less than in part (a), so it
    had to be $2n - 1$)

    (c) $a = 12, d = -2$
    So n^{th} term $= dn + (a - d) = -2n + (12 + 2) = \mathbf{-2n + 14 \text{ (or } 14 - 2n)}$

    Eeeek...Watch out for the minus signs in part (c).
    Two minus signs together make a plus.

2   Numbers of dots are 1, 3, 6, 10….
    Differences are 2, 3, 4...
    So, $a = 1, d = 2, C = 1$

    n^{th} term $= 1 + ((n - 1) \times 2) + (\frac{1}{2}(n - 1)(n - 2) \times 1)$

    $= 1 + 2n - 2 + \frac{1}{2}(n^2 - 3n + 2)$

    $= 1 + 2n - 2 + \frac{1}{2}n^2 - 1\frac{1}{2}n + 1$

    $= \mathbf{\frac{1}{2}n + \frac{1}{2}n^2 \text{ (or } \frac{1}{2}n(n + 1))}$

    You might recognise this sequence — they're the triangular numbers.

3 (a) n^2. You should have spotted that these are the square numbers.
    If you didn't, you can get the same answer by using the formula
    $a + (n - 1)d + \frac{1}{2}(n - 1)(n - 2)C$.

    (b) $a = 3, d = 2$
    So, n^{th} term $= dn + (a - d) = 2n + (3 - 2) = \mathbf{2n + 1}$

    (c) This sequence comes from multiplying the terms of the other sequences
    together. So n^{th} term $= \mathbf{n^2(2n + 1)} \ \ \mathbf{(or \ 2n^3 + n^2)}$.

Page 29

1 (a) 10

    (b) $-5 + -7 - 6 = -5 - 7 - 6 = \mathbf{-18}$

    (c) $10 - -4 + 5 = 10 + 4 + 5 = \mathbf{19}$

    (d) -4

    (e) $-4 \times -100 \div -25 = -4 \times 4 = \mathbf{-16}$

2 (a) $-11x$

    (b) $(4x - -5x) \div (-2 - 1) = 9x \div -3 = \mathbf{-3x}$

    (c) $8y \div -4 + -8x \div 2 = -2y + -4x = \mathbf{-2y - 4x}$

3 (a) $x^2y = (-4)^2 \times 3 = 16 \times 3 = \mathbf{48}$

    (b) $(xy)^2 = (-4 \times 3)^2 = (-12)^2 = \mathbf{144}$

    (c) $x^2 - y^2 = (-4)^2 - 3^2 = 16 - 9 = \mathbf{7}$

    (d) $y^3 + x^3 - 2xy = 3^3 + (-4)^3 - (2 \times -4 \times 3) = 27 + - 64 - -24 = \mathbf{-13}$

    BODMAS is what you need here — brackets, other, division, multiplication, addition,
    subtraction. 'Other' means stuff like squaring, making tea, going to the loo, etc.

Page 30

1   $d = st + \frac{1}{2}at^2$

    $= (2 \times 10) + (\frac{1}{2} \times 0.5 \times 10^2)$

    $= 20 + 25$

    $= \mathbf{45 \ m}$

2 (a) $T = \dfrac{75W + 990}{11}$ (b) $W = \dfrac{5P}{11}$

    $= \dfrac{(75 \times 4) + 990}{11}$ $= \dfrac{5 \times 16.5}{11} = \dfrac{82.5}{11} = 7.5$ kg

    $= \dfrac{300 + 990}{11}$ $T = \dfrac{75W + 990}{11}$

    $= \mathbf{117 \ minutes}$ $= \dfrac{(75 \times 7.5) + 990}{11}$

                       $= \dfrac{562.5 + 990}{11} = \dfrac{1552.5}{11} = \mathbf{141 \ minutes}$

      Get your maths wrong here and you'll end up with no Christmas dinner.

3
$$H = AC^2 + 2B - \frac{2B+C}{3A}$$

$$= 2(-3)^2 + (2 \times 10\frac{1}{2}) - \frac{(2 \times 10\frac{1}{2}) + -3}{3 \times 2}$$

$$= 18 + 21 - \frac{(21-3)}{6}$$

$$= 39 - 3 = \mathbf{36}$$

Page 31

1

x	x^3	$5x^2$	$x^3 - 5x^2$	$x^3 - 5x^2 + 3$	
0	0	0	0	3	Too big
1	1	5	−4	−1	Too small
0.7	0.343	2.45	−2.107	0.893	Too big
0.8	0.512	3.2	−2.688	0.312	Too big
0.9	0.729	4.05	−3.321	−0.321	Too small
0.85	0.614125	3.6125	−2.998375	0.001625	Too big

The answer is between 0.85 and 0.9. So, to 1 decimal place, it's **0.9**.

2
$$y(y + 1)(4y - 2) = 28\ 120$$

You aren't given any values of y, so guess some:

E.g. Try $y = 10$

$10(10 + 1)(4(10) - 2) = 10 \times 11 \times 38 = 4180$ — much too small.

Try $y = 100$

$100(100 + 1)(4(100) - 2) = 100 \times 101 \times 398 = 4\ 019\ 800$ — too big.

Try $y = 50$

$50(50 + 1)(4(50) - 2) = 50 \times 51 \times 198 = 504\ 900$ — still much too big.

Try $y = 20$

$20(20 + 1)(4(20) - 2) = 20 \times 21 \times 78 = 32\ 760$ — too big.

Try $y = 15$

$15(15 + 1)(4(15) - 2) = 15 \times 16 \times 58 = 13\ 920$ — too small.

Try $y = 18$

$18(18 + 1)(4(18) - 2) = 18 \times 19 \times 70 = 23\ 940$ — too small.

Try $y = 19$

$19(19 + 1)(4(19) - 2) = 19 \times 20 \times 74 = 28\ 120$ — the answer.

So, $y = \mathbf{19}$

Trial and error is a fiddly nuisance. It's really important to put down everything you did to find the answer though, or you won't pick up all those lovely marks.

Page 32

1 (a) $2x + 8 = 4 - 6x$

$2x + 8 - 2x = 4 - 6x - 2x$

$8 = 4 - 8x$

$8 - 4 = -8x$

$x = \frac{4}{-8} = -\frac{1}{2}$

(b) $6(x - 1) = 42$

$\frac{6(x-1)}{6} = \frac{42}{6}$

$x - 1 = 7$

$x - 1 + 1 = 7 + 1$

$x = \mathbf{8}$

(c) $4 - 10x = 9$

$4 - 10x + 10x = 9 + 10x$

$4 = 9 + 10x$

$4 - 9 = 9 + 10x - 9$

$-5 = 10x$

$x = -\frac{1}{2}$

(d) $\frac{6}{2x - 1} = 2$

$\frac{6(2x-1)}{2x-1} = 2(2x-1)$

$6 = 2(2x - 1)$

$6 = 4x - 2$

$8 = 4x$

$x = \frac{8}{4} = \mathbf{2}$

(e) $4 - \frac{12}{5x-1} = 6$

$4 - \frac{12}{5x-1} - 4 = 6 - 4$

$-\frac{12}{5x-1} = 2$

$-\frac{12(5x-1)}{5x-1} = 2(5x-1)$

$-12 = 10x - 2$

$-12 + 2 = 10x - 2 + 2$

$-10 = 10x$

$x = -\frac{10}{10} = \mathbf{-1}$

You can do whatever you like to equations, just as long as you do exactly the same to BOTH sides.

Page 33

1 (a) $4(x - 2) - 2(3 - 2x) = 5x + 1$

$4x - 8 - 6 + 4x = 5x + 1$

$3x = 15$

$x = \mathbf{5}$

(b) $\frac{6}{2x-1} = \frac{8}{3x-2}$

$6(3x - 2) = 8(2x - 1)$

$18x - 12 = 16x - 8$

$2x = 4$

$x = \mathbf{2}$

(c) $\sqrt{1 - 2x} = 3$

$1 - 2x = 9$

$2x = -8$

$x = \mathbf{-4}$

2 (a) $\sqrt{x^2 + 7} = x + 1$

(b) $x^2 + 7 = (x + 1)^2$

$x^2 + 7 = (x + 1)(x + 1)$

$x^2 + 7 = x^2 + 2x + 1$

$7 - 1 = x^2 + 2x - x^2$

$6 = 2x$

$x = \mathbf{3}$

If you've got an equation to solve with a square root sign in it, the first thing to do is get rid of the square root sign. Do this by squaring both sides of the equation.

Page 34

1 (a) $V = \frac{1}{3}\pi r^2 h$

$3V = \pi r^2 h$

$h = \frac{3V}{\pi r^2}$

(b) $V = \frac{1}{3}\pi r^2 h$

$3V = \pi r^2 h$

$r^2 = \frac{3V}{\pi h}$

$r = \sqrt{\frac{3V}{\pi h}}$

2 (a) $F = 1.8C + 32$

$F - 32 = 1.8C$

$C = \frac{F - 32}{1.8}$

(b) $C = \frac{80 - 32}{1.8} = \mathbf{26.7\ °C}$

3
$$d = st + \frac{1}{2}at^2$$

$2d = 2st + at^2$

$at^2 = 2d - 2st$

$a = \frac{2d - 2st}{t^2} = \frac{2(d - st)}{t^2}$

Never try to rearrange equations like this in one go. If you do, you're doomed. You've got to do them step by step, writing down your new equation each time.

8

Page 35

1 (a) $\frac{300}{0.02} = \mathbf{15\,000\ kg/m^3}$ (b) $\frac{1800}{0.6} = \mathbf{3000\ kg/m^3}$

2 (a) $70 \times 4 = \mathbf{280\ km}$ (b) $15 \times 3.5 = \mathbf{52.5\ km}$

  (c) 15 minutes = 0.25 hours

      $160 \times 0.25 = \mathbf{40\ miles}$

3   20 tonnes = 20 000 kg $\frac{20\,000}{800} = \mathbf{25\ m^3}$

4   4 pm to 7 pm = 3 hours $\frac{180}{3} = \mathbf{60\ mph}$

Page 36

1 (a) A = (–2, 2), B = (–4, –1), C = (2, –1)

  (b) D = (4, 2)

  (c) Area = 6 × 3 = **18 sq. units**

2 (a) B = (4, 0, 0), R = (4, 3, 2), S = (0, 3, 2), P = (0, 0, 2)

  (b) AB = (2, 0, 0)

     CD = (2, 3, 0)

     SR = (2, 3, 2)

Once you get your head round them, 3-D coordinates aren't as hard as they look. Remember — put the coordinates in the right order, (x, y, z).

Page 37

1 (a)   (b) (i) $\frac{1}{4}$ (ii) $-\frac{3}{5}$ or –0.6

2 (a) and (b)

   (a) B may be anywhere along this line.

   (b) Q may be anywhere along this line.

Check your lines are in the right direction — positive gradients slope up, negative gradients slope down.

3   Change in $y = 4a - 2a = 2a$ Change in $x = 10 - 4 = 6$

     Gradient $= \frac{2a}{6} = 2$ $a = \mathbf{6}$

Page 38

1 (a) $84 (accept \$83-85)

  (b) 84 ÷ 50 = 1.68 (accept 1.66-1.70)

  (c) $1.68 per £ (accept $1.66-1.70 per £)

2   B

On distance-time graphs, the gradient is the speed. You normally travel lots faster by train than you do cycling or walking, so you'd expect the middle part of the graph to be the steepest.

Page 39

1    $y = 2$ line AB $x = -2$ line AD

     $y = x$ line DB $y = -2$ line DC

     $y = -x$ line AC

2 (a) Q   (b) S   (c) R   (d) P   (e) T

Page 40

1 (a) Graph A $y = 5 - 2x$ Graph B $y = x^2 + 5$

     Graph C $y = \frac{2}{x}$ Graph D $y = x - 3$

(b) $(y = x^3)$

2   A(0, –1)   B(0, 10)   C(0, 4)   D(–3, 0)

On these graphs, you don't know what the scale is. So, you have to work out where they cross the axes using just the equation. If you want to know the intersection with, say, the y-axis, just bung x = 0 into the equation and find out what y is.

Page 41

1 (a)

x	0	3	5
y	–2	7	13

  (b)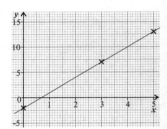

  (c) $\left(\frac{2}{3}, 0\right)$

2 (a) $y = 4 - x$

  (b)

x	0	2	4
y	4	2	0

  (c)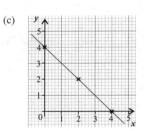

Page 42

1 (a) and (b)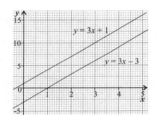

              $y = 3x + 1$

              $y = 3x - 3$

  (c) $y = 3x - 3$

2 (a)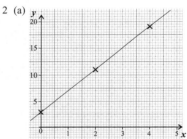

  (b) $a = 4,\ b = 3$

3 (a) $y = \frac{x}{2}$ or $2y = x$ (b) $y = -\frac{x}{2} + 4$ or $2y = 8 - x$

Plotting straight line graphs is pretty simple really. They've all got the general equation y = mx + c — m is the gradient and c is where it crosses the y-axis. Remember that and you're sorted.

Page 43

1 (a)

x	–3	–2	–1	0	1	2	3
y	–9	–11	–11	–9	–5	1	9

(b)

(c) −11.5 (accept −11.25 to −12)   (d) −2 (accept −1.5 to −2.5)

(a)

x	−3	−2	−1	0	1	2	3
y	41	25	13	5	1	1	5

(b)

(c) $x = 1.5$

If you plot your points and they're not in a nice straight line or a smooth curve, you know something's gone wrong somewhere. Check you've plotted your points accurately and that you worked out the numbers in the table of values correctly.

Page 44

(a)

Litres (L)	0	10	20	30	40
Cost (C)	0	7.50	15.00	22.50	30

(b)

These axes are pretty similar. Make sure you read their labels before you start plotting points.

(c) (i) £20.25 (accept £19.25-21.25)

(ii) 37.3 litres (accept 36.3 to 38.3)

2 (a) ¾ hour / 45 minutes   (b) 10:15

(c) $30 \div \frac{1}{2} = \mathbf{60\ mph}$ (d) 50 mph

Page 45

1 (a) $(x + 6)(x + 2)$ (b) $(x + 16)(x + 1)$

(c) $(x − 2)(x − 2) = (x − 2)^2$ (d) $(x − 5)(x + 3)$

2 (a) $x = 2$ or $x = 3$ (b) $x = −1$ or $x = 2$

(c) $(x + 10)(x − 1) = 0$, $\mathbf{x = −10\ or\ x = 1}$

(d) $(x + 6)(x + 7) = 0$, $\mathbf{x = −6\ or\ x = −7}$

3 (a) $x^2 + 3x − 4 = 0$, $(x − 1)(x + 4) = 0$, $\mathbf{x = 1\ or\ x = −4}$

(b) $x^2 − 6x + 8 = 0$, $(x − 2)(x − 4) = 0$, $\mathbf{x = 2\ or\ x = 4}$

(c) $x^2 + 7x + 10 = 0$, $(x + 2)(x + 5) = 0$, $\mathbf{x = −2\ or\ x = −5}$

For added fun, these quadratic equations usually have two solutions. You'll need to put both of them to get all the marks on offer.

Page 46

1 (a) $3x + y = 10$ (eq.1)

$x + y = 4$ (eq.2)

(eq.1) − (eq.2)

$2x = 6$

$\mathbf{x = 3}$

substitute x in (eq.1)

$(3 \times 3) + y = 10$

$\mathbf{y = 1}$

(b) $12x − 11y = 23$ (eq.1)

$x + y = 0$ (eq.2)

$11 \times$ (eq.2) $= 11x + 11y = 0$ (eq.3)

(eq.1) + (eq.3)

$23x = 23$

$\mathbf{x = 1}$

substitute x in (eq.2)

$1 + y = 0$

$\mathbf{y = −1}$

(c) $y = 3x + 1$ rearranges to $3x − y = −1$ (eq.1)

$2x + 5y = 22$ (eq.2)

$5 \times$ (eq.1) $= 15x − 5y = −5$ (eq.3)

(eq.2) + (eq.3)

$17x = 17$

$\mathbf{x = 1}$

substitute x in (eq.1)

$(3 \times 1) − y = −1$

$\mathbf{y = 4}$

2 (a) 3 coffees + 2 teas = £2.70 $3c + 2t = 2.70$ (eq.1)

1 coffee + 1 tea = £1.10 $c + t = 1.10$ (eq.2)

$2 \times$ (eq.2) $= 2c + 2t = 2.20$ (eq.3)

(eq.1) − (eq.3)

$c = 0.50$

substitute in (eq.2) $0.5 + t = 1.10$ $t = 0.6$ So, 1 cup of tea costs **60p**

(b) 3 red pens + 5 blue pens = £2.15 $3r + 5b = 2.15$ (eq.1)

2 red pens + 1 blue pen = £0.85 $2r + 1b = 0.85$ (eq.2)

$5 \times$ (eq.2) $= 10r + 5b = 4.25$ (eq.3)

(eq.3) − (eq.1) $= 7r = 2.10$

$r = 0.3$ So, 1 red pen costs **30p**

Page 47

1 (a)

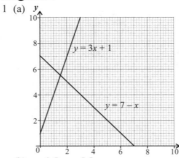

(b) $x = 1.5$, $y = 5.5$

2 (a) $x = 2$, $y = 6$ (b) $x = 0$, $y = 4$ (c) $x = 1$, $y = 2$

Simultaneous equations are dead easy to solve with graphs. The solution is just the x and y values at the point where the graphs cross.

Page 48

1 (a) $x < 4$ (b) $2x < 2$, $x < 1$ (c) $7x < 28$, $x < 4$

(d) $5x \geq 30$, $x \geq 6$ (e) $6x \leq 30$, $x \leq 5$ (f) $−x > −6$, $x < 6$

(g) $x < −3$ (h) $−3x \geq 9$, $x \leq −3$

(i) $13x − 15x > 21 − 5$, $−2x > 16$, $x < −8$

(j) $4x − 5x \geq 13 − 12$, $−x \geq 1$, $x \leq −1$

2 (a) $x < 4$

(b) $2x < 2$, $x < 1$

(c) $4x > −4$, $x > −1$

Solving inequalities is just like solving normal equations — except for one thing. When you divide by a negative number, you have to flip the inequality sign, so it points in the other direction.

Page 49

1

2
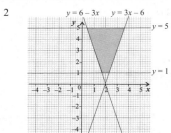

3   $y > 2$, $y < 3x + 1$ and $y < 8 - 2x$

Pages 50, 51, 52 and 53

1 (a) $3x$ (b) $x - 6$

2 (a) $2x^2 + 2x + 4x + 24 = \mathbf{2x^2 + 6x + 24}$

  (b) $3x^2 - x - 21x + 7 = \mathbf{3x^2 - 22x + 7}$

  (c) $(3x + 5)(3x + 5) = 9x^2 + 15x + 15x + 25 = \mathbf{9x^2 + 30x + 25}$

3 (a) A = (1, 3), B = (2, 5), C = (6, 2)

  (b) (i) 2   (ii) $-\dfrac{3}{4}$

4 (a) $6(2x + 3)$ (b) $6b(2a + b)$ (c) $5xy^2\,(3x^3y + 1)$

5 (a) $c = \dfrac{(3+1)^2}{2} = \mathbf{8}$ (b) $b = \dfrac{(x+a)^2}{c} = \dfrac{(6+2)^2}{4} = \mathbf{16}$

  Part (a) is just a case of bunging the numbers into the equation. Part (b) is a tiny bit more tricky. You've got to rearrange the equation first to make b the subject.

6 (a) $8x + 12 = 4x + 16$
    $8x - 4x = 16 - 12$
    $4x = 4$
    $\mathbf{x = 1}$

  (b) $\dfrac{3}{2x+1} = \dfrac{1}{x-1}$
    $3(x - 1) = 1(2x + 1)$
    $3x - 3 = 2x + 1$
    $\mathbf{x = 4}$

7 (a) $y^2 + 5 = x$ (b) $3y + 5x + 10 = 0$
    $y^2 = x - 5$ $3y = -5x - 10$
    $\mathbf{y = \sqrt{x - 5}}$ $\mathbf{y = \dfrac{-5x - 10}{3}}$

8 (a) 26, 37, 50 (the difference increases by 2 each time)

  (b) 8, 13, 21 (add the previous 2 terms each time)

9 (a) $a = 6$, $d = 5$
    n^{th} term $= dn + (a - d) = 5n + (6 - 5) = \mathbf{5n + 1}$

  (b) n^{th} term $= a + (n - 1)d + \tfrac{1}{2}(n - 1)(n - 2)C$, where $a = 2$, $d = 6$ and $C = 4$.
    $= 2 + ((n - 1) \times 6) + (\tfrac{1}{2}(n - 1)(n - 2) \times 4) = 2 + 6n - 6 + 2(n - 1)(n - 2)$
    $= 2 + 6n - 6 + 2n^2 - 6n + 4 = \mathbf{2n^2}$

  Once you think you know what the nth term is, it's a good idea to check your answer by using it to work out terms you already know for sure. So try things like n = 2 and n = 3 and see if it works.

10 (a) $12 - x \geq 20$ (b) $3 + 2x < 33 + 5x$
     $-x \geq 8$ $3 - 33 < 5x - 2x$
     $\mathbf{x \leq -8}$ $-30 < 3x$
                                     $\mathbf{x > -10}$

11
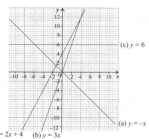

12 (a) $(x - 5)(x - 6) = 0$ (b) $(x - 1)(x + 7) = 0$
      $\mathbf{x = 5 \text{ or } x = 6}$ $\mathbf{x = 1 \text{ or } x = -7}$

13 (a)

  (b) $x = 1$, $y = 4$

  (c) $y - 3x = 1$ (eq.1)
    $y - x = 3$ (eq.2)
    (eq.2) − (eq.1) $= 2x = 2$
    $\mathbf{x = 1}$
    substitute in (eq.1)
    $y - (3 \times 1) = 1$
    $\mathbf{y = 4}$

14
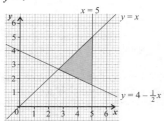

  The first thing you have to do here is convert each inequality into an equation. Then you can draw the lines on the graph. The bit you want will be the bit enclosed by these lines.

Page 54

1

x	x^3	$x^3 + x$	
0	0	0	Too small
3	3	30	Too big
1	1	2	Too small
2	8	10	Too small
2.5	15.625	18.125	Too big
2.2	10.648	12.848	Too big
2.1	9.261	11.361	Too small
2.15	9.938	12.088	Too big

  $\mathbf{x = 2.1}$

2 (a) 3.86 kg = 3860 g

    density $= \dfrac{\text{mass}}{\text{volume}} = \dfrac{3860}{200} = 19.3$ g/cm^3

    So, the metal is **gold**.

  (b) volume $= \dfrac{\text{mass}}{\text{density}} = \dfrac{200}{7.9} = \mathbf{25.3\ cm^3}$

3 (a) 20 minutes is one third of an hour.
    In 1 hour Andy can run 12.6 km.

    So, in 20 minutes Andy can run $\dfrac{12.6}{3} = \mathbf{4.2\ km.}$

  (b) 8190 m = 8.19 km

    time $= \dfrac{8.19}{12.6} = 0.65$ hours

    $0.65 \times 60 = \mathbf{39\ minutes}$

    Watch out for units when you're dealing with density and speed formulas.

Section Three — Shapes

Page 55

1 (a) heptagon (b) 7 (c) 7

2   Exterior angle $= \dfrac{360°}{5} = 72°$
    Interior angle $= 180° - 72° = \mathbf{108°}$

(a) Angle at centre = exterior angle, so $x = \dfrac{360°}{8} = \mathbf{45°}$ (b) $y = \mathbf{45°}$

Interior angle = 180° − Exterior angle

$150° = 180° - \dfrac{360°}{\text{Number of sides}}$

$\dfrac{360°}{\text{Number of sides}} = 180° - 150°$

$\dfrac{360°}{30°} = $ Number of sides $= \mathbf{12}$

So remember — Exterior angle = 360° divided by the number of sides.

Angle at centre = exterior angle

Interior angle = 180° minus exterior angle

Page 56

(a)
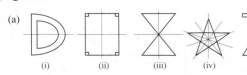

(i) (ii) (iii) (iv) (v)

(b) (i) 1 (ii) 2 (iii) 2 (iv) 5 (v) 2

7

Page 57

(a) 2, 1, 1 (b) 2, 1

90°, 45° and 45°

(a) tetrahedron (b) cone (c) cuboid

(a) triangular prism (b) cylinder (or circular prism) (c) square-based pyramid

sphere

There's no two ways about it, I'm afraid. You've just got to learn these shape names.

Page 58

(a) Area $= \dfrac{1}{2} \times$ base $\times$ height $\dfrac{1}{2} \times 8 \times 3 = \mathbf{12\ m^2}$

(b) Area $= 8 \times (10 - 3) = 8 \times 7 = \mathbf{56\ m^2}$

The two triangles on the ends are the same size, so the area of the shape is the same as that of a rectangle. $8 \times 9 = \mathbf{72\ cm^2}$

Area $= \dfrac{1}{2} \times (9 + 13) \times 6 = \mathbf{66\ cm^2}$

Page 59

Circumference $= \pi d = 865\,000 \times 3.14 \approx \mathbf{2\,716\,000\ miles}$

Diameter $= 2r$, so radius $= \dfrac{80}{2} = 40$ cm

Area $= \pi r^2 = 3.14 \times 40^2 = \mathbf{5024\ cm^2}$

Circumference $= 2\pi r = 2 \times 3.14 \times 1.6 = \mathbf{10.048\ m}$

What's the point of circles, I ask myself.

Page 60

1   Length of missing side = 9 − 3 − 4 = 2 m

So perimeter = 9 + 5 + 3 + 2 + 4 + 3 + 2 + 4 = **32 m**

2 (a) Circumference of semicircle $= \dfrac{1}{2} \times \pi d = \dfrac{1}{2} \times 3.14 \times 6 = 9.42$ cm

Perimeter of whole shape = 9.42 + 14 + 10 + 6 = **39.4 cm** (3 s.f.)

(b) Area of semicircle $= \dfrac{1}{2} \times \pi r^2 = \dfrac{1}{2} \times 3.14 \times 3^2 = 14.13$ cm^2

Area of square = 6 cm × 6 cm = 36 cm^2

Area of triangle $= \dfrac{1}{2} \times (14\ \text{cm} - 6\ \text{cm}) \times 6\ \text{cm} = \dfrac{8\ \text{cm} \times 6\ \text{cm}}{2} = 24$ cm^2

Total area = **74.1 cm²** (3 s.f.)

It helps to fill in all the information you know on the diagram as you find it out.

3   Area of rectangle = 25 cm × 8 cm = 200 cm^2

Area of larger circle $= \pi \times 3^2 = 3.14 \times 9 = 28.26$ cm^2

Area of smaller circle $= \pi \times 1.5^2 = 3.14 \times 2.25 = 7.065$ cm^2

Total area = Area of rectangle − Areas of two circles

Total area = 200 cm^2 − 28.26 cm^2 − 7.065 cm^2 = **165 cm²** (3 s.f.)

Page 61

1   18 cm^2 × 6 cm = **108 cm³**

2   2.4 m × 0.8 m × 0.5 m = **0.96 m³**

3 (a) Area of circle $= \pi r^2$, diameter $= 2r$

$r = \dfrac{7.4}{2} = 3.7$

$A = 3.14 \times 3.7^2 = \mathbf{43.0\ cm^2}$ (3 s.f.)

(b) Volume = 11 cm × 43.0 cm^2 = **473 cm³** (3 s.f.)

4

FORMULA	LENGTH	AREA	VOLUME
D	✓		
a^2l			✓
$2R$	✓		
r^2h			✓
lw		✓	

A formula for length will never have any lengths multiplied together.
A formula for area will always have two lengths multiplied together.
A formula for volume will always have three lengths multiplied together.
Remember that lengths can be multiplied by themselves, so R^2 counts as two lengths multiplied together.

Page 62

1 (a) 6 (b) 5 (c) 9

2   $(2 \times 3 \times 8) + (2 \times 3 \times 5) + (2 \times 8 \times 5) = \mathbf{158\ cm^2}$

3

Page 63

1   $a = 180° - 60° - 40° = \mathbf{80°}$

$b = 180° - 25° - 80° = \mathbf{75°}$

2   Angles c and d must be the same, because they are in an isosceles triangle. To find c and d, you must first find the other angle in the triangle. This angle must be $180° - 90° = 90°$.

$c + d + 90° = 180°$ $c + d = 90°$, but $c = d$, so $c = \mathbf{45°}$ and $d = \mathbf{45°}$

$e = 180° - 40° = \mathbf{140°}$

3 (a) $\angle ACB = 180° - 90° - 24° = \mathbf{66°}$

(b) $\angle DCE = 180° - 80° - 66° = \mathbf{34°}$

(c) $\angle DEC = 180° - (2 \times 34°) = \mathbf{112°}$

4 $x = 180° - 100° - 30° = \textbf{50°}$

To find y, you must first find the other angle in the triangle:

$180° - 50° - 100° = 30°$

$y = 180° - 40° - 30° = \textbf{110°}$

In order to find z, you must first find p and q.

$p = 180° - 40° = 140°$ $q = 180° - 100° - 30° = 50°$

$z = 360° - 130° - 140° - 50° = \textbf{40°}$

Page 64

1 (a) ∠CBG and ∠AGF are supplementary angles.

∠AGF = $180° - 110° = \textbf{70°}$

(b) ∠CBG and ∠DEB are alternate angles.

∠DEB = **110°**

(c) ∠DEC = $180° - 110° = 70°$

∠ACB = $180° - 52° - 70° = \textbf{58°}$

(d) ∠ABC and ∠AGF are corresponding angles, so ∠ABC = 70°

∠CAG = $180° - 70° - 58° = \textbf{52°}$

2 (a)

(b) Angle q and ∠FAB are alternate angles, so $q = 24°$

Angle p and ∠FED are alternate angles, so $p = 68°$

$x = p + q = \textbf{92°}$

(c) By the same principle as (b), $y = r + s = 69° + 40° = \textbf{109°}$

Page 65

1 (a) ∠BAD = 90° (angle in a semicircle) and angles of triangle ABD add up to 180°.

(b) If BC = CD, then ∠CDB = ∠CBD = 45°. $58° + 45° = \textbf{103°}$

2 (a) 90°. The angle between the tangent and the radius is always 90°.

(b) ∠OBD = $90° - x$ ∠ODB = $90° - x$ (isosceles triangle)

∠DOB $= 180° - (90° - x) - (90° - x) = 2x$ (angles of triangle)

Page 66

1 (a) A and C are congruent.   (b) A, C and D are similar.

2 (a) Larger rocket is $\dfrac{20}{15} = \dfrac{4}{3}$ times the size of the smaller rocket.

$57 \text{ cm} \times \dfrac{4}{3} = \textbf{76 cm}$

(b) Smaller rocket is $\dfrac{15}{20} = \dfrac{3}{4}$ times the size of the larger rocket.

$12 \text{ cm} \times \dfrac{3}{4} = \textbf{9 cm}$

(c) 42°

Remember that angles stay the same when a shape is enlarged.

Page 67

1   Area factor = $3^2 = 9$ Area = $16.4 \times 9 = \textbf{147.6 cm}^2$

2   Scale factor = 2, so volume factor = $2^3 = 8$ Weight = $10 \times 8 = \textbf{80 lb}$

3

4 (a) $\dfrac{6}{4} = \textbf{1.5}$ (b) (4, 2)

(c) Scale factor = 1.5, so area factor = $1.5^2 = 2.25$

$10 \times 2.25 = \textbf{22.5 cm}^2$

Page 68

1 (a) $\begin{pmatrix} 2 \\ 0 \end{pmatrix}$ (b) $\begin{pmatrix} 3 \\ 4 \end{pmatrix}$ (c) $\begin{pmatrix} 2 \\ -3 \end{pmatrix}$ (d) $\begin{pmatrix} -2 \\ 3 \end{pmatrix}$ (e) $\begin{pmatrix} 0 \\ -3 \end{pmatrix}$ (f) $\begin{pmatrix} -5 \\ -4 \end{pmatrix}$

2 (a) and (b)

(c) $\begin{pmatrix} 1 \\ -3 \end{pmatrix}$ (d) $\begin{pmatrix} -5 \\ -1 \end{pmatrix} + \begin{pmatrix} 6 \\ -2 \end{pmatrix} = \begin{pmatrix} 1 \\ -3 \end{pmatrix}$

Page 69

1 (a) Through 90° anticlockwise about the origin.

(b) Through 90° clockwise about the origin.

(c) Through 180° about the origin.

2 (a) and (b)

(c) (i) Rotation through 90° anticlockwise about the origin.

(ii) Rotation through 180° about the origin.

(d) Rotational symmetry of order 4

Page 70

1 (a) (i) x-axis or $y = 0$ (ii) $y = x$ (iii) $x = 1$

(b) Rotation through 90° clockwise about the origin.

2 (a), (b) + (c)

(d) Reflection in $y = -x$

Page 71

1 (a) $x^2 = 12^2 + 16^2$

$x = \textbf{20 m}$

(b) $17^2 = y^2 + 8^2$

$y = \textbf{15 cm}$

2   Distance $= \sqrt{10^2 - 3^2} = \sqrt{91} = \textbf{9.54 m}$

3 (a) Angle C = 90° (angle in a semicircle)

(b) BC $= \sqrt{9^2 - 6.2^2} = \sqrt{42.56} = \textbf{6.52 cm}$

$$h = \sqrt{37^2 - 12^2} = \sqrt{1225} = 35 \text{ cm}$$
$$\text{Total Area} = 12 \times 35 = \mathbf{420 \text{ cm}^2}$$

Page 72

(a) 1 cm = 1 km

(b) 245° (± 2°)   (c) 4 km (± 0.1km)

(a) ½ cm = 1 km

(b) 010° (± 2°)

Page 73

$$\sin x = \frac{1.5}{2.6} \qquad x = \sin^{-1}\left(\frac{1.5}{2.6}\right) = \mathbf{35.2°} \text{ (3 s.f.)}$$

$$\tan x = \frac{240}{670} \qquad x = \tan^{-1}\left(\frac{240}{670}\right) = \mathbf{20°}$$

(a) $\tan 15 = \dfrac{3}{a}$

$a = \dfrac{3}{\tan 15°} = \mathbf{11.2 \text{ m}}$

(b) $\sin 15 = \dfrac{3}{\text{ramp length}}$

$\text{ramp length} = \dfrac{3}{\sin 15} = \mathbf{11.6 \text{ m}}$

Page 74

(a) $\cos 47° = \dfrac{1.5}{BC} \qquad BC = \dfrac{1.5}{\cos 47} = \mathbf{2.20 \text{ m}}$

(b) $BC = BA$
    $2 \times 2.20 \text{ m} = \mathbf{4.40 \text{ m}}$

(a) $\tan \theta = \dfrac{100}{160} \qquad \theta = \tan^{-1}\left(\dfrac{100}{160}\right) = \mathbf{32°}$

(b) $\cos 40 = \dfrac{100 \text{ cm}}{r} \qquad r = \dfrac{100 \text{ cm}}{\cos 40} = \mathbf{131 \text{ cm}}$

$\tan 55° = \dfrac{\text{Height of steeple}}{9} \qquad \text{Height of steeple} = 9 \times \tan 55° = \mathbf{12.85 \text{ m}}$

Page 75

Use a sharp pencil for this type of question.

Pages 76, 77 and 78

1

2 (a) 6 cm × 4 cm = **24 cm²**   (b) $\frac{1}{2} \times 6$ cm × 3 cm = **9 cm²**

(c) 24 cm² + 9 cm² = **33 cm²**

3 (a) 5 × 8 cm = **40 cm**

(b) Sum of exterior angles = 360° $\dfrac{360°}{5} = \mathbf{72°}$

(c) Interior angle = 180° − 72° = **108°**

4

5

6 (a) ∠ABC = 90° (angle in a semicircle)

(b) ∠OCD = <ODC = 90° − 35° = **55°**

(c) ∠COD = 180° − (2 × 55°) = **70°**

7 (a) 70° (corresponding angle)   (b) 180° − 70° = **110°**

(c) 180° − 70° − 80° = **30°** (corresponding angle with the angle between 80° and a)

(d) 180° − 30° = **150°**

8 (a) cuboid, rectangular prism or square prism

(b) (i) pentagons   (ii) Another rectangle

9 $4rst + t^3$ **V** $2rd + 4st + 5qp$ **A** $d + 2e + 4c$ **L**

$2s^2 + 3dt$ **A** $3p(r^2 + st)$ **V**

Page 79

1    $\tan \theta = \dfrac{12 \text{ cm}}{20 \text{ cm}} \qquad \theta = \tan^{-1}\dfrac{12}{20} = \mathbf{31°}$

2 (a) $\text{Area} = \dfrac{1}{2}\pi r^2 = \dfrac{1}{2} \times 3.14 \times 6^2 = \mathbf{56.5 \text{ cm}^2}$ (3 s.f.)

(b) Volume = 56.52 cm² × 15 cm = **848 cm³** (3 s.f.)

Keep the un-rounded figure for the area in part (a) in your calculator ready for part (b).

3    $AC = \sqrt{30^2 + 50^2} = \sqrt{3400} = \mathbf{58.3 \text{ cm}}$ (3 s.f.)

*Remember that any diagram you come across will always be made up of **simple shapes**.*

Section 4 — Statistics & Probability

Page 80

1 $1 - 0.05 = \mathbf{0.95}$

2 $1 - \left(\dfrac{1}{8} + \dfrac{1}{4}\right) = \dfrac{\mathbf{5}}{\mathbf{8}}$

3 $\dfrac{1}{3} = \dfrac{5}{15}, \dfrac{2}{5} = \dfrac{6}{15}, \dfrac{6}{15} > \dfrac{5}{15}$ So, **card B** is more likely to win.

4 (a) $1 - \dfrac{3}{8} = \dfrac{\mathbf{5}}{\mathbf{8}}$ (b) $\dfrac{3}{8}$ (c) $\dfrac{2}{7}$

Part (b) is a bit of a trick question. If he takes a chocolate out, but puts it back without eating it, the probabilities are all the same as they were originally. Nothing's changed.

Page 81

1 Soup, Lasagne, Ice-Cream
Soup, Lasagne, Trifle
Soup, Fish, Ice-cream
Soup, Fish, Trifle
Soup, Chicken, Ice-cream
Soup, Chicken, Trifle
Melon, Lasagne, Ice-cream
Melon, Lasagne, Trifle
Melon, Fish, Ice-cream
Melon, Fish, Trifle
Melon, Chicken, Ice-Cream
Melon, Chicken, Trifle

2 (a) $\dfrac{4}{6} = \dfrac{\mathbf{2}}{\mathbf{3}}$ (b) $\dfrac{1}{2} \times \dfrac{1}{2} = \dfrac{\mathbf{1}}{\mathbf{4}}$

3 (a) 7492, 7942, 7294, 7924   (b) $\dfrac{3}{4}$

There's a pretty high probability that you'll get tested on this stuff at some time or other, so keep at these questions until you can do them all.

Page 82

1 (a) $\dfrac{1}{6}$ (b) $\dfrac{1}{6} \times 600 = \mathbf{100}$

2 The theoretical probability of getting heads is ½ but the estimated probability is only $^{350}/_{1000}$. This is much less than ½, so the coin is not fair — there isn't an equal chance of getting a head or a tail.

3 (a) $\dfrac{6}{30} = \dfrac{\mathbf{1}}{\mathbf{5}}$ (b) $\dfrac{15}{90} = \dfrac{\mathbf{1}}{\mathbf{6}}$ (c) $\dfrac{1}{5} \times 120 = \mathbf{24\ times}$

Page 83

1 (a) independent   (b) mutually exclusive

2 (a) $\dfrac{1}{6} + \dfrac{1}{6} = \dfrac{2}{6} = \dfrac{\mathbf{1}}{\mathbf{3}}$ (b) $\dfrac{1}{4} \times \dfrac{1}{4} = \dfrac{\mathbf{1}}{\mathbf{16}}$ (c) $\dfrac{1}{13} \times \dfrac{4}{51} = \dfrac{\mathbf{4}}{\mathbf{663}}$

You need a bit of general knowledge about playing cards for this one. There's 52 cards in a deck (without the jokers). The deck's divided into 4 suits — hearts, clubs, spades and diamonds. These suits all have 13 cards in them — ace, the numbers 2-10, jack, queen and king. So next time you're playing cards, you can claim you're brushing up on your maths.

3 (a) $0.65 \times 0.65 = 0.4225 \approx \mathbf{0.423}$ (3 s.f.)
(b) $0.35 \times 0.35 = 0.1225 \approx \mathbf{0.123}$ (3 s.f.)
(c) $(0.65 \times 0.35) + (0.35 \times 0.65) = \mathbf{0.455}$

Page 84

1 (a)

(b) $0.16 + 0.24 + 0.24 = \mathbf{0.64}$ (or $1 - 0.36 = \mathbf{0.64}$)

2 (a)
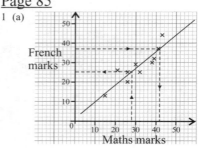

(b) $\dfrac{12}{42} + \dfrac{12}{42} = \dfrac{24}{42} = \dfrac{\mathbf{4}}{\mathbf{7}}$ (c) $\dfrac{12}{42} + \dfrac{6}{42} = \dfrac{18}{42} = \dfrac{\mathbf{3}}{\mathbf{7}}$

Tree diagrams are amazingly useful for loads of probability questions. Even if the question doesn't actually tell you to draw one, it can be helpful to draw one anyway.

Page 85

1 (a)
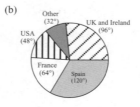

(b) See diagram.   (c) moderate positive correlation
(d) 25 marks (accept 22-28)   (e) 42 marks (accept 39-45)

Page 86

1 (a)

Destination	Frequency	Angle of sector (°)
UK and Ireland	12	**96** (12 ÷ 45 × 360)
Spain	15	**120** (15 ÷ 45 × 360)
France	8	**64** (8 ÷ 45 × 360)
USA	6	**48** (6 ÷ 45 × 360)
Other	4	**32** (4 ÷ 45 × 360)

(b)

Other (32°)
UK and Ireland (96°)
USA (48°)
France (64°)
Spain (120°)

2 $40 \div 20 = 2°$ per teenager
$360 \div 2 = \mathbf{180\ teenagers}$

Pie charts are probably the most difficult type of graph to draw. If your angles all add up to 360° you know you're on the right track though.

Page 87

1 (a) 9   (b) 9   (c) $22 - 3 = \mathbf{19}$

2 (a) mean $= \dfrac{(100 + 12 + 4 + 4)}{4} = \mathbf{£30}$
median = £8
mode = £4

(b) The best average is the median as 3 out of 4 responses were £12 or under. The mean is too big and the mode is too small.

3 Let x be the third score.
$\dfrac{(25 + 32 + x)}{3} = 30$
$25 + 32 + x = 90$
$x = \mathbf{33}$

This is where algebra comes in really handy. Write an equation, then rearrange it and find the missing number. Hey presto — that's the problem solved.

Page 88

1 (a)

Number of TVs	Frequency	Number of TVs × Frequency
1	55	55
2	68	136
3	75	**225**
4	25	**100**
5	15	**75**
6	8	**48**
7	4	**28**
TOTALS	250	667

(b) 250   (c) $667 \div 250 = \mathbf{2.67}$ (3 s.f.)   (d) 3

(e) The middle value is between the 125th and 126th frequency values. Median = **3.**

(f) $7 - 1 = \mathbf{6}$

Page 89

1 (a)

Age in years	Frequency (f)	Mid-Interval Value (x)	f × x
15 to 19	125	17½	2187½
20 to 24	85	22½	1912½
25 to 29	40	27½	1100
30 to 34	35	32½	1137½
35 to 39	15	37½	562½
TOTALS	300	—	6900

mean age = $6900 \div 300 = \mathbf{23\ years}$

(b) 15 to 19

(c) The middle value is between the 150th and 151st frequency values. The median age group is **20 to 24**

2 $\dfrac{(30 \times 7) + (90 \times 12) + (150 \times 22) + (210 \times 9)}{50} = \dfrac{6480}{50} = \mathbf{129.6\ minutes}$

Page 90

1

Expenditure in pence (x)	Frequency	Cumulative Frequency
$0 \le x < 50$	2	**2**
$50 \le x < 100$	2	**4**
$100 \le x < 150$	**18**	22
$150 \le x < 200$	**54**	76
$200 \le x < 250$	10	**86**
$250 \le x < 300$	**14**	100

2 (a)

Heights in cm (h)	Tally	Frequency	Cumulative Frequency
$140 \le h < 150$	||||	4	4
$150 \le h < 160$	|||| ||	7	11
$160 \le h < 170$	|||| ||||	10	21
$170 \le h < 180$	||||	4	25
$180 \le h < 190$	||	2	27

(b) The median is the 14th value. Median group is $\mathbf{160 \le h < 170}$.

On this question, it's dead easy to miss a few numbers out as you do your tally. So, cross out the numbers as you go, and you'll know you've got them all.

Page 91

1 (a)

Page 91 (right column continued)

(b) (i) 162 cm (accept 160-164 cm)

(ii) 155 cm (accept 153-157 cm)

(iii) 169 cm (accept 167-171 cm)

(iv) $169 - 155 = \mathbf{14\ cm}$ (or answer (iii) – answer (ii))

(c) 16 pupils (accept 15-17 pupils)   (d) 3 pupils (accept 2-4 pupils)

Cumulative frequency curves are CURVES. So no using a ruler to join the points.

Pages 92 and 93

1 (a) $1 - \dfrac{1}{4} = \dfrac{\mathbf{3}}{\mathbf{4}}$

(b) 3 counters. There must be 3 times more blue counters than there are green.

(c) $2 \times 3 = \mathbf{6\ counters}$

(d) 8 out of 20 are yellow ($\frac{2}{5}$) and at least 1 must be red. So the greatest number of pink counters possible is $20 - 8 - 1 = \mathbf{11}$.

2    $\dfrac{(3x + 10 + 2x + 5 + x - 3)}{3} = 20$

$6x + 12 = 60$

$x = 8$

Game 1 = $(3 \times 8) + 10 = \mathbf{34\ points}$, Game 2 = $(2 \times 8) + 5 = \mathbf{21\ points}$, Game 3 = $8 - 3 = \mathbf{5\ points}$

3 (a) $(4 \times 0) + (6 \times 1) + (8 \times 2) + (n \times 3) + (1 \times 4) = 26 + 3n$

(b) $4 + 6 + 8 + n + 1 = \mathbf{19 + n}$

(c) $\dfrac{26 + 3n}{19 + n} = 2$

$26 + 3n = 2(19 + n)$

$26 + 3n = 38 + 2n$

$\mathbf{n = 12}$

4

Page 94

1 (a) $0.06 \times 0.06 = \mathbf{0.0036}$

(b) $(0.94 \times 0.06) + (0.06 \times 0.94) = \mathbf{0.113}$ (3 s.f.)

(c) $0.06 \times 60 = 3.6$ wooden mirrors estimated to split. She probably **will** have enough wood to make 55 mirrors without splits.

The wood either splits or it doesn't, so the probabilities of these two things must add up to 1. The probability that the wood splits is 0.06, so the probability that it doesn't is 0.94. Use your calculator if you're a bit dicey at decimals.

2

Number of days absent	Frequency (f)	Cumulative Frequency	Midpoint (x)	f × x
0 to 4	32	32	2	64
5 to 9	67	99	7	469
10 to 14	131	230	12	1572
15 to 19	43	273	17	731
20 to 24	7	280	22	154

(a) See table above.

(b) See table above. The median is between the 140th and 141st value. The median group is **10 to 14** days absence.

(c) $2990 \div 280 = \mathbf{10.7}$ (3 s.f.) days

ISBN 978 1 84146 526 5

9 781841 465265

MHQA31

Coordination Group Publications